Introduction

What did you think of science when you were a child? I have a hazy recollection of my early experience of the subject. Most of the time, at secondary level, science seemed to mean cramming knowledge into our heads, and then having tests to see if we remembered it all.

This feeling about science remained with me until I entered teacher training college. From that moment on, my eyes were gradually opened as I experienced the 'hands on' approach to learning about science. For 17 years I taught in three primary schools in the Bristol area, spending the last six years as headteacher of a village school.

I left the teaching profession in 1986 to pursue my interest in magic on a full-time basis. I have slowly graduated through the ranks in the magical world and am now a Member of The Inner Magic Circle. I lecture a lot on the subject, and a large part of my work involves visiting primary schools with my Creative Magic and Science Fun shows.

The Science Fun show has two main aims:

- to enable the children to realise that science is fun;
- to prove it is fun by doing experiments.

Throughout each performance I am always asking the children questions, probing the extent of their knowledge, and filling in the missing gaps where appropriate.

DEVELOPING SKILLS

The contents of this book are based upon my Science Fun show, which demonstrates practical ideas in science that the children can try for themselves. These ideas are designed to encourage the development of practical, manipulative, thinking and reasoning skills. These include:

- observing;
- following instructions accurately;
- making predictions and testing them;
- practising construction and manipulative skills;
- communicating through speech, writing and pictures;
- stating ideas and theories and testing them;
- using knowledge and practical skills to solve problems.

You may well recognise many of the experiments, and may have tried them out for yourself. I hope that you will also discover some ideas that are new to you, or some interesting modifications of old ideas. All the experiments have been tried and tested, and *they do work*!

At the end of each activity is a note of the relevant attainment targets covered. I have also given an approximate age range for each experiment. However, this is only a rough guide. Children vary; as a class teacher you know your children, and will be able to select the experiments that will best suit their needs.

During the last few years I have organised a number of Science INSET days. Time and time again two areas of concern have been expressed by teachers:

- 'How can one teach science with a class of thirty or more children?'
- 'How can we manage when we have so little in the way of resources?'

TEACHING METHODS

Teaching science with a class of thirty children can be a difficult task. Teaching is a personal thing, and a teacher develops with experience. There is no set way to teach science, because there are so many variables. It depends upon the teacher's personality and teaching skills, the attitude of the children, the level of help and resources, and so on. Some teachers are more confident and effective when teaching on a formal whole-class basis; others prefer teaching in small groups, while others prefer a blend of teaching methods depending upon the subject and situation.

Ideally, teachers should try out any experiment in advance, and iron out any snags, so that they feel confident when demonstrating it. It is also useful to have the appropriate material at hand for any follow-up work.

When an experiment is presented to the whole class it can be put over as a sort of challenge: 'What happens if . . .?' Children will then be using their thinking and reasoning skills to solve the problem.

Let's take as an example the 'Swinging pendulums' activity on page 61. This has endless possibilities. The children could be asked to predict what would happen if you started one of the pendulums swinging. When they have found out, they could make suggestions for other investigations; for example, what happens if the pendulums are placed wide apart, if one of them is made lighter, if the string is shortened, and so on. These suggestions could be noted down, and during the day groups of children could try out their ideas and report back on their findings.

I am not in favour of children writing up all their experiments, except perhaps for a selected few, to make use of written and pictorial skills. Verbal presentations and discussions provide other ways of recording children's activities.

School assemblies can be a good opportunity for children to talk about and demonstrate some of their experiments. Overhead projectors are a useful visual aid for illustrating optical illusions, and in general, the more varied the approach, the more fun the presentation will be. At the same time, the children will be enhancing their language development.

RESOURCES

Much of the work that goes on in primary science does not require costly equipment. In my last school we compiled two lists of items needed; one for the items we could get for free, such as corks, wool, bottles and so on, and the other for items that had to be purchased. We based our strategy for acquiring resources on these two lists.

To house the 'free' resources we collected about a hundred large ice cream containers. Each one was labelled clearly with its contents, and allocated space on a shelf. This resource area also housed the items that were purchased. They were kept in drawers and cupboards, all very clearly labelled. In a large school this system might be a little difficult to set up, but it could possibly be adapted for certain areas of a school.

It is a good idea to build up a science reference library, including books to which teachers can refer. A comprehensive science policy, well-organised resources, a good reference library and support from colleagues will boost the confidence of most teachers.

I recently came across an amusing definition of science: 'If it smells, it's chemistry; if it moves, it's biology; if it doesn't work, it's physics'. Perhaps these experiments are the exception that proves the rule, since although most of them would probably have to be classified as physics, they certainly all work!

Have fun.

Tony Griffith

Magic or science?

Many magical tricks rely on skill and sleight of hand to achieve the desired effect. However, the 'tricks' in this section all have a scientific explanation.

Most children love magic tricks and watching magicians. Better still, they like doing tricks themselves, and they should have fun with the ones in this section. Doing tricks and performing will give the children confidence in themselves and in their ability to communicate.

Jumping paper-clips

Objectives
To demonstrate an unusual phenomenon in which two paper-clips link together, and to set a couple of problems to be solved.

Age range
Eight to eleven.

Group size
Individuals or pairs.

What you need
A £5 note or a piece of paper of similar size for each group, paper-clips.

What to do
First, demonstrate the trick to the class. Fold the £5 note into three as shown. Take the two paper-clips and fix them to the note. The illustration will help you to position them correctly. Pull the two ends of the note to straighten it out. The paper-clips link up as they meet and jump into the air, linked together. (A word of warning: don't pull the note too quickly, or it may tear!)

Next, help the children to do the trick for themselves.

Follow-up
When they have mastered the linking of two paper-clips, see if the children can work out how to link three paper-clips, and then four.

This trick can also be done with the large plastic paper-clips that can be obtained from good stationers. In such a case it is preferable that larger pieces of thin card be used instead of paper.

Scientific notes
This trick relies on a topological phenomenon called transference of curves. What happens is that the S-shaped curve made by the folds in the £5 note is transferred to the paper-clips when the note is straightened. If you do the trick slowly you will see what happens.

Science AT1, 10

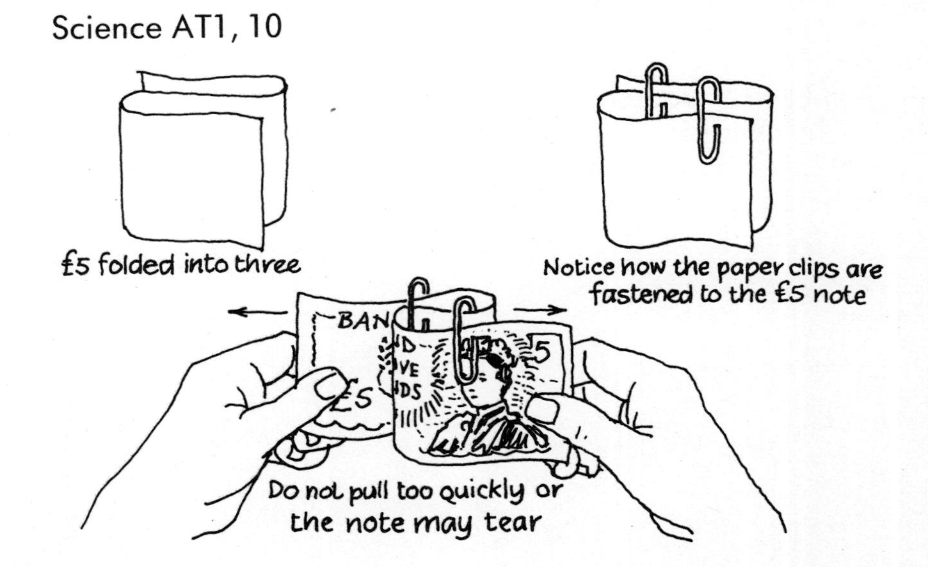

Catch the £5 note

Objective
To test reaction times.

Age range
Seven to eleven.

Group size
Pairs.

What you need
Several £5 or play bank notes, a ruler with 'HOLD HERE' marked at one end and 'WAIT HERE' marked at the other – these can be written on sticky paper.

What to do
One child from each pair should hold the bank note in her right hand. The other should place his thumb and fingers on either side of the note (as illustrated). Explain that the first child should drop the bank note and her partner must try to catch it. He is not to attempt to catch it until she releases if.

The children will find that they are unable to catch the note; they will be clutching thin air and the bank note will flutter to the floor. Ask them to swap over to prove the difficulty of the task.

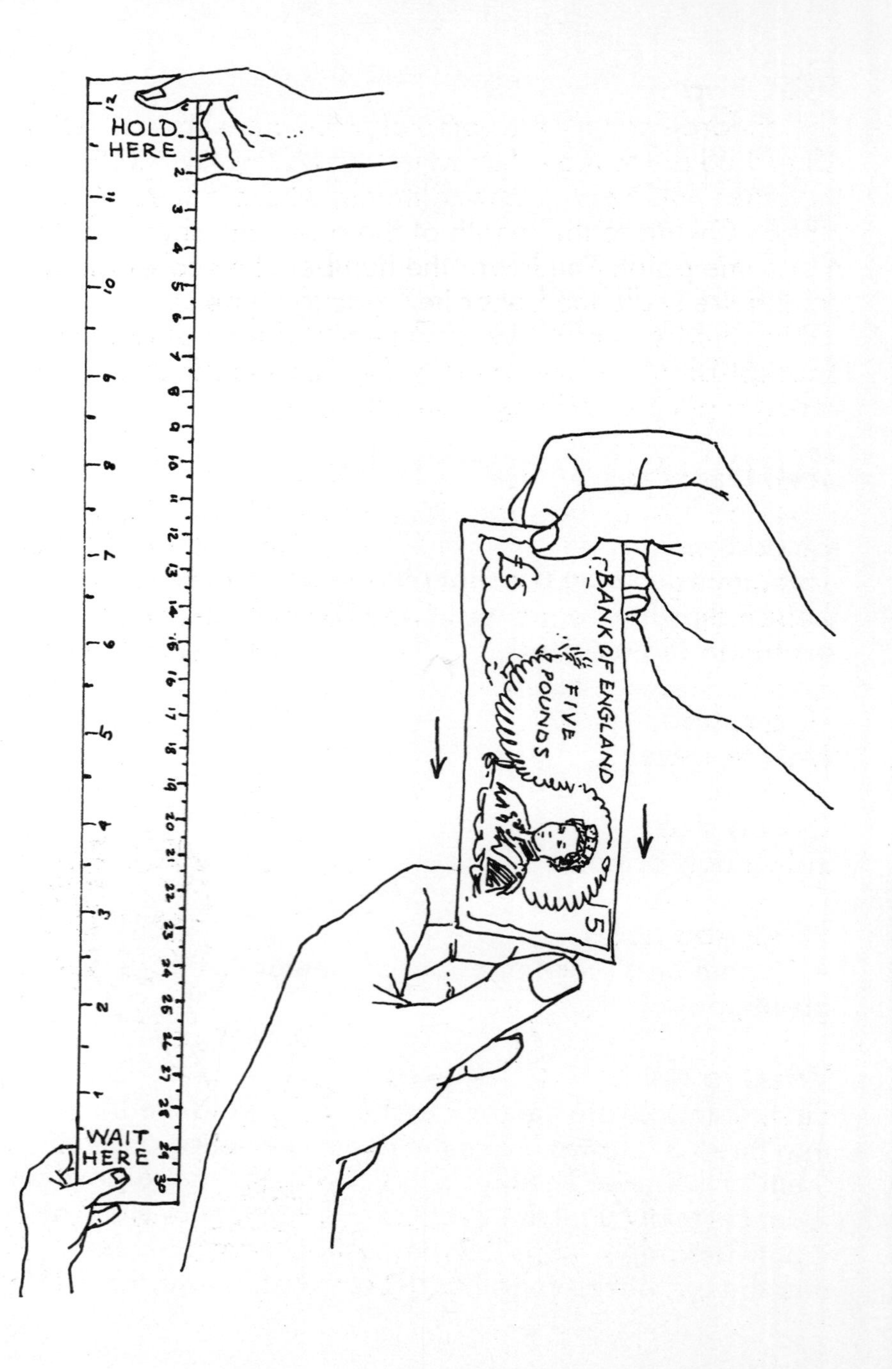

Follow-up

The children can try the same experiment with a ruler. One child holds the ruler where it says 'HOLD HERE'; the other puts her finger and thumb where it says 'WAIT HERE'. Owing to the length of the ruler, she should catch it at some point. The lower the number she scores on the centimetre scale the better her reaction time is.

The children could devise a series of tests of reaction speeds using the ruler and try them on their friends, recording their findings in graph form.

Scientific notes

Provided the catchers do not close their fingers before the bank note is released, they will never catch it. By the time they see the note fall, and send the signal to close their fingers, the response always comes a fraction of a second too late and the reaction time will invariably be too slow to catch the note.

Science AT1, 2

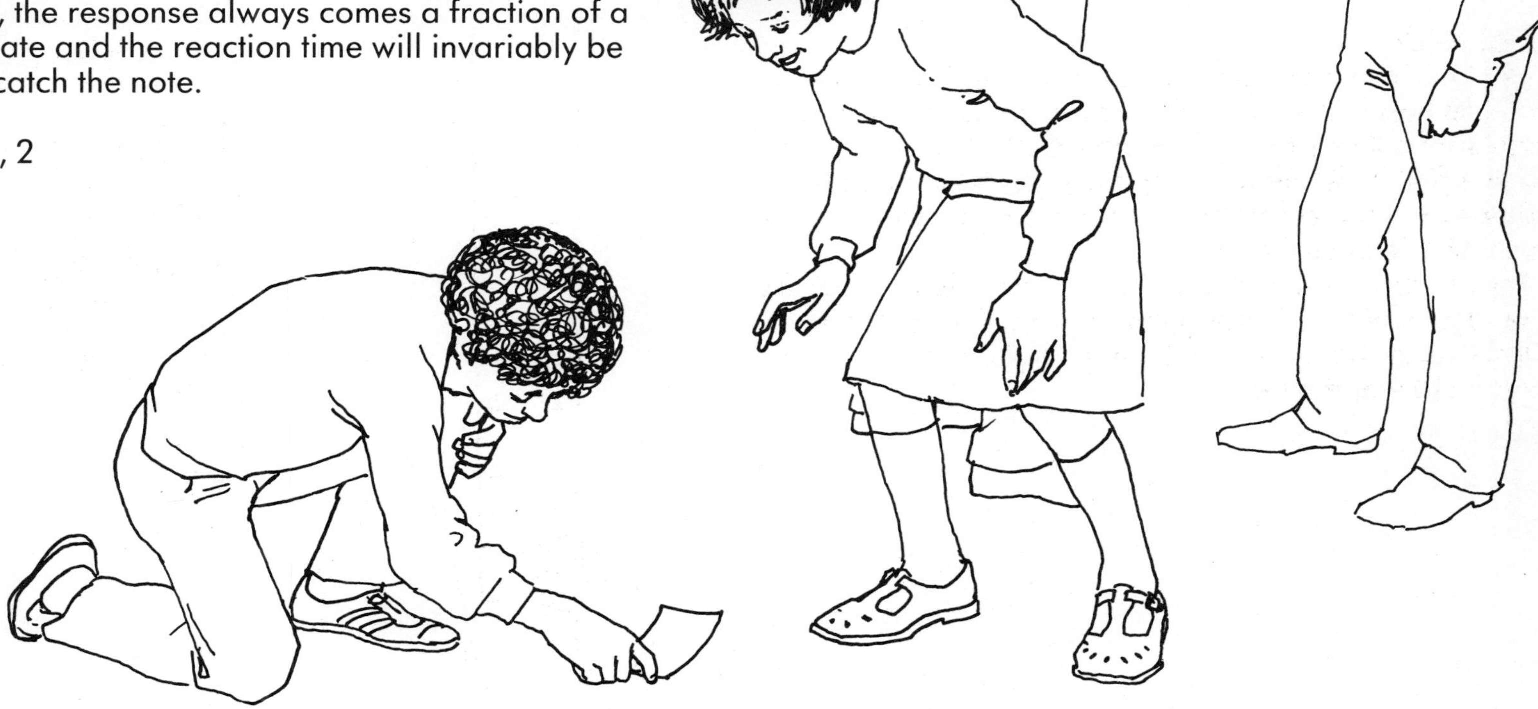

Magical propellers

Objective
To show how vibrations can cause a cardboard propeller to spin and change direction.

Age range
Ten to eleven.

Group size
Pairs.

What you need
Pieces of wooden dowelling about 15 to 18cm long, cardboard propellers, drawing pins, small thin sticks (about the size of a pencil).

What to do
The children should carefully cut some notches in the wooden dowelling and fix the cardboard propeller to one end with the drawing pin as shown.

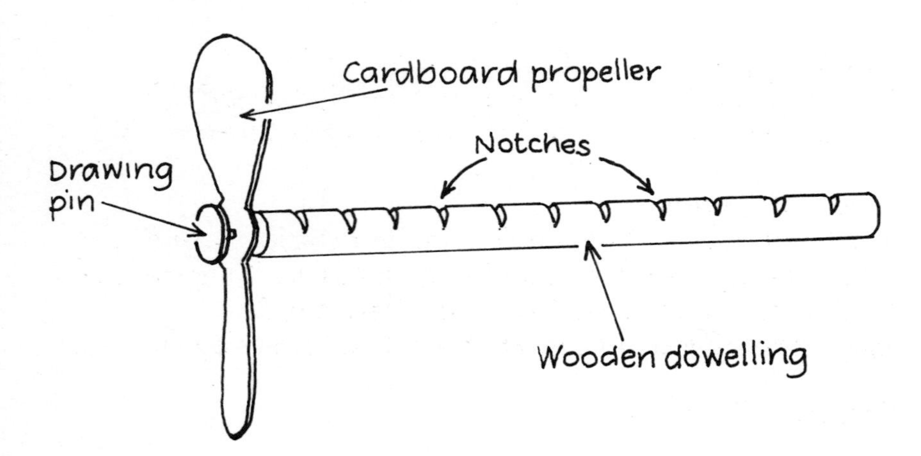

Next, the children should hold the stick in the right hand, *forefinger on top, thumb at the side*, and rub the notches firmly and quickly with the stick. As they rub, their forefinger must be *on top of the stick and directly over the notches*, but their thumb must not touch the dowelling. The propeller will spin round in a clockwise direction. While they are rubbing and the propeller is spinning, the children should slide the stick across the notches so that the right thumb comes into contact with the dowelling. The propeller should now spin in an anti-clockwise direction.

Scientific notes
The propeller spins because the rubbing causes a vibration which follows a circular path. When the thumb comes into contact with the wooden dowelling, the direction of this circular path is reversed.

Science AT1, 10

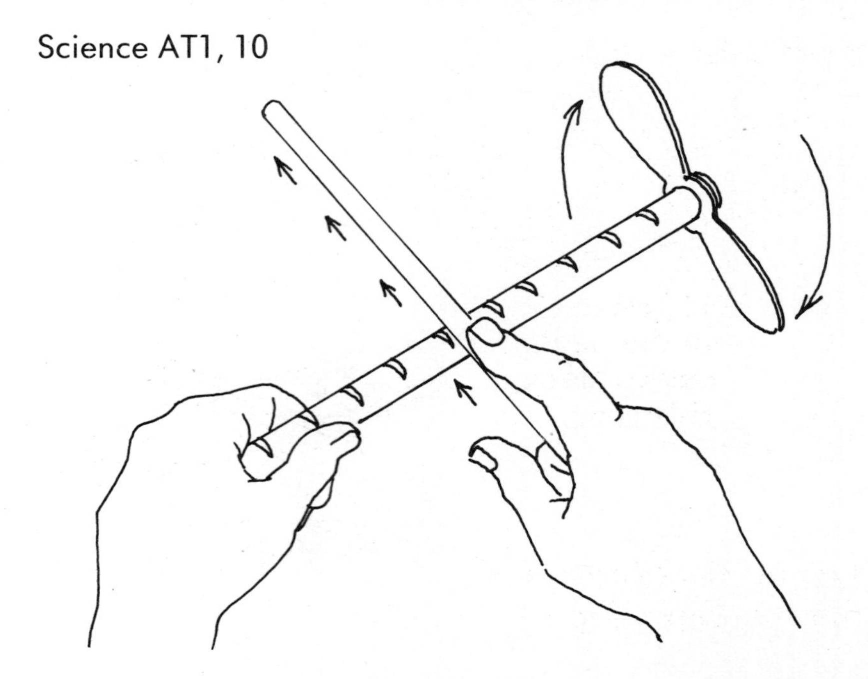

Magical matchstick

Objective
To create an optical illusion in which a matchstick appears to pass through a safety pin.

Age range
Eight to eleven.

Group size
Individuals or pairs.

What you need
Safety pins, matchsticks (without heads).

What to do
The safety pin should be pushed through the *centre* of the matchstick, as shown in the illustration, and closed.

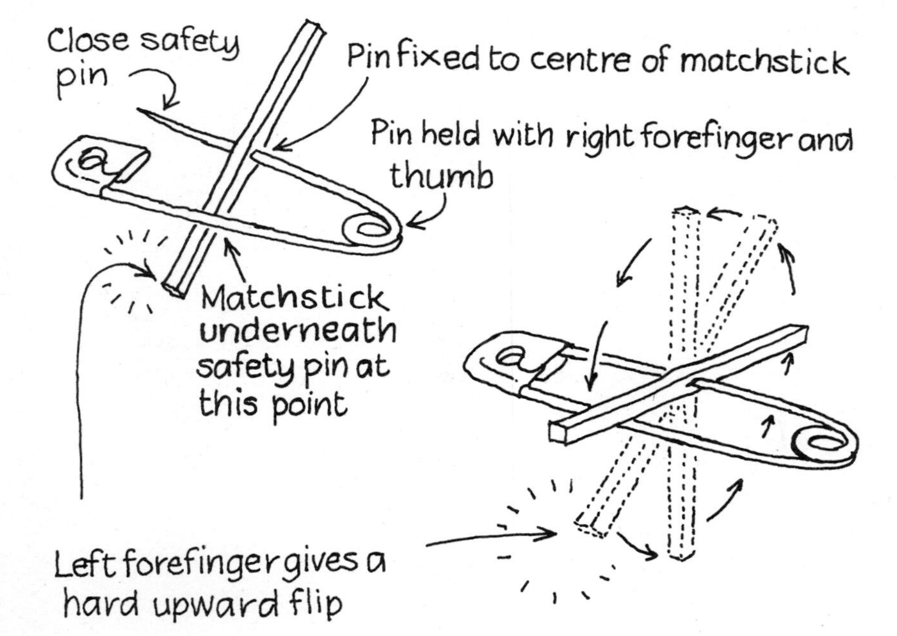

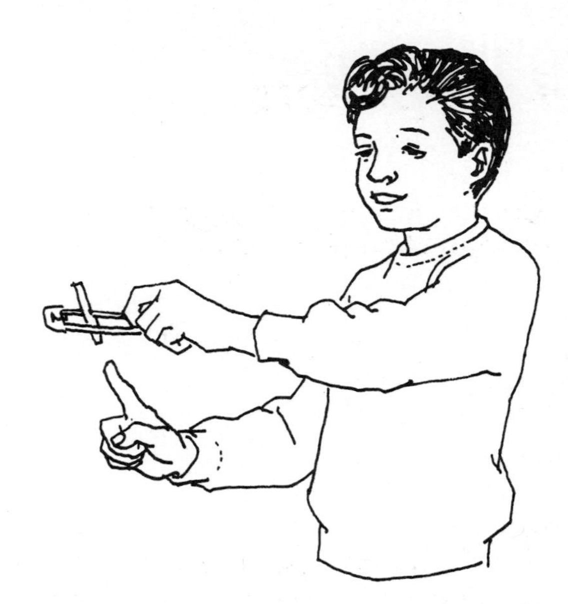

The safety pin can then be held at one end between the right forefinger and thumb. The bar of the safety pin should be on top and nearest the body, with the matchstick underneath. The children should now bring the left forefinger up beneath the end of the matchstick nearest the body, and give it a hard upward flip. The matchstick will appear to pass through the safety pin.

Follow-up
See if the children can make a similar trick, perhaps using a wire coat-hanger and a thin piece of dowelling.

Scientific notes
The hard upward snap makes the matchstick spring back and fly round the other way. Because it happens so fast, it appears to penetrate the safety pin. The movement of the matchstick is too fast for the eye to see.

Science AT1, 2

The mighty knife

Objective
To lift a jar of rice with a knife.

Age range
Nine to eleven.

Group size
Pairs or small groups.

What you need
Glass jars and other containers (each with a body wider than its opening), uncooked rice, table knives.

What to do
First the children should fill the jar to the very top with rice, packing the grains down with their hands. Next, they should push a knife straight down into the rice, going down no further than 10cm, pull it out and repeat the action about ten times. Finally, they should push the knife as far down as it can go. This time, when they lift the knife, the jar of rice should cling to it. **This experiment should only be done under adult supervision.**

Follow-up
Try this with different jars, utensils other than knives, and other foodstuffs such as peas, beans and lentils.

Scientific notes
Each time the knife is pushed into the rice, the grains are rearranged and packed more tightly together. If enough grains wedge themselves against the knife and the top of the jar, it should be possible to lift the knife so that the jar of rice will cling to it.

Science AT1, 6

The magic cup

Objective
To show how a paper cup will appear magically to adhere to a knife.

Age range
Nine to eleven.

Group size
Pairs.

What you need
A paper drinking cup, a table knife and a small magnet for each pair.

What to do
One child should secretly drop the magnet into the paper cup. Then he can pick up the paper cup and, without showing its inside, place it on the blade of the knife, which he should hold in his other hand. The magnet will immediately be attracted to the blade of the knife through the paper of the cup.

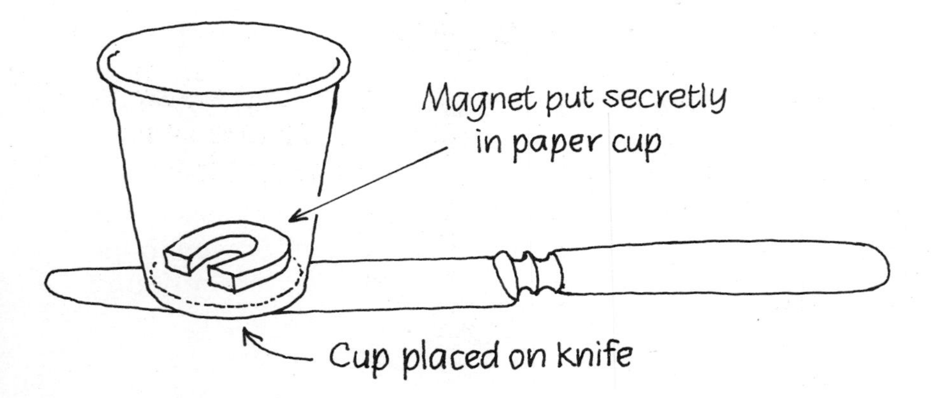

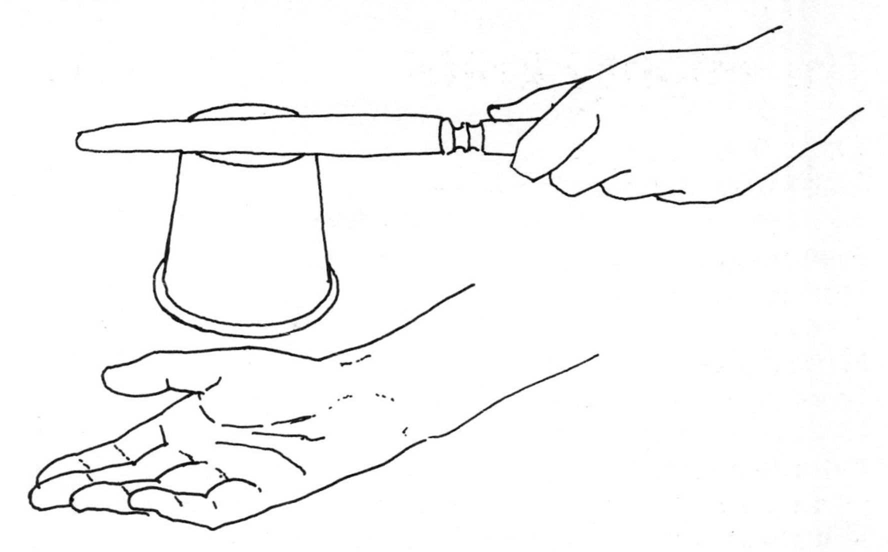

If the child then places his hand over the mouth of the cup, and inverts the cup and knife, keeping his hand in place, his partner will probably think that his hand is keeping the cup in place against the knife (particularly if he 'acts up' the situation). He can then remove his hand; the cup 'magically' remains suspended.

The child should then turn everything back to its original position, handing the knife out for inspection. Meanwhile, he can allow the magnet to fall into his hand and secretly put it in his pocket.

Follow-up
- Ask the children to try this experiment with a china cup. Will it still work?
- Does the strength of the magnet make any difference?

Scientific notes
The power of the magnetic force works through the bottom of the paper cup, holding the magnet to the knife.

Science AT1, 11

Unpoppable balloons

Objective
To show that it is possible to stick a pin in a balloon without bursting it.

Age range
Nine to eleven.

Group size
Pairs or small groups.

What you need
Balloons, sticky tape, pins, scissors.

What to do
Get the children to inflate their balloons, but tell them not to blow them up too hard.

Next they should stick a piece of adhesive tape on to the balloon, and then take a pin and very carefully push it through the tape. The children may be surprised to observe that the pin will go right through the tape and the balloon, without bursting it.

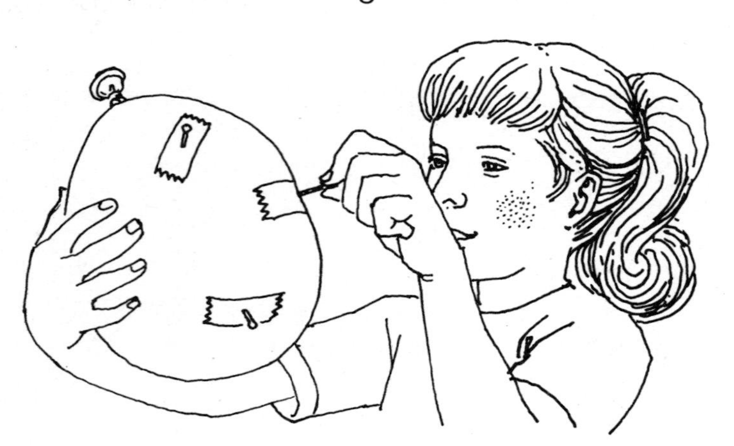

Follow-up
- Using sticky tape, let the children find out how many pins they can stick in a balloon without it bursting, and what happens if they remove the pins.
- What happens if the children carefully stick a pin in the dark spot at the end of a balloon?

Scientific notes
Normally, a balloon will burst when a pin is stuck into it. As the pin penetrates the balloon, the air rushes out with a bang and the rubber shrivels up. However, the sticky tape changes the nature of the material, holding the rubber together and preventing the balloon bursting.

The dark spot on the end of a balloon is thicker than the rest of the balloon, and acts in a similar way to the sticky tape. If the pin is stuck in carefully, the balloon shouldn't burst.

Science AT1, 6

Seeing through a brick

Objective
To demonstrate how a beam of light from a torch can apparently go through a brick.

Age range
Nine to eleven.

Group size
Pairs or small groups.

What you need
For each group, a torch, a piece of card with a slit in it, Plasticine, eight mirrors, two building bricks.

What to do
Challenge the group to shine the torch so that the light appears to go through the brick.

When they give up, show them how to set up the apparatus as shown, using four of the mirrors.

Ask one child to shine the torch through the slit in the card. The torch light will bounce from one mirror to another. It will look as though the beam of light has come through the solid brick.

Follow-up
- Ask the children to use the rest of the mirrors and see if they can arrange the apparatus so that the beam of light goes round two bricks.
- Can the children work out how to send a beam of light from one room to another using the same principle?
- When they have worked this out, ask them to use Morse code to send a message.

Scientific notes
Light will not shine through objects that are opaque. Light travels in straight lines, and will not bend around corners. To make it appear to travel through the brick, it has to be bounced off a series of mirrors.

The torch light shining through the slit in the card bounces off the first mirror and on to the second. It is then bounced on to the third mirror, and so on. By carefully arranging the mirrors it is possible to make the torch light go around the brick. This principle is also used to reflect the sun's rays on to solar heat collectors.

Science AT1, 15

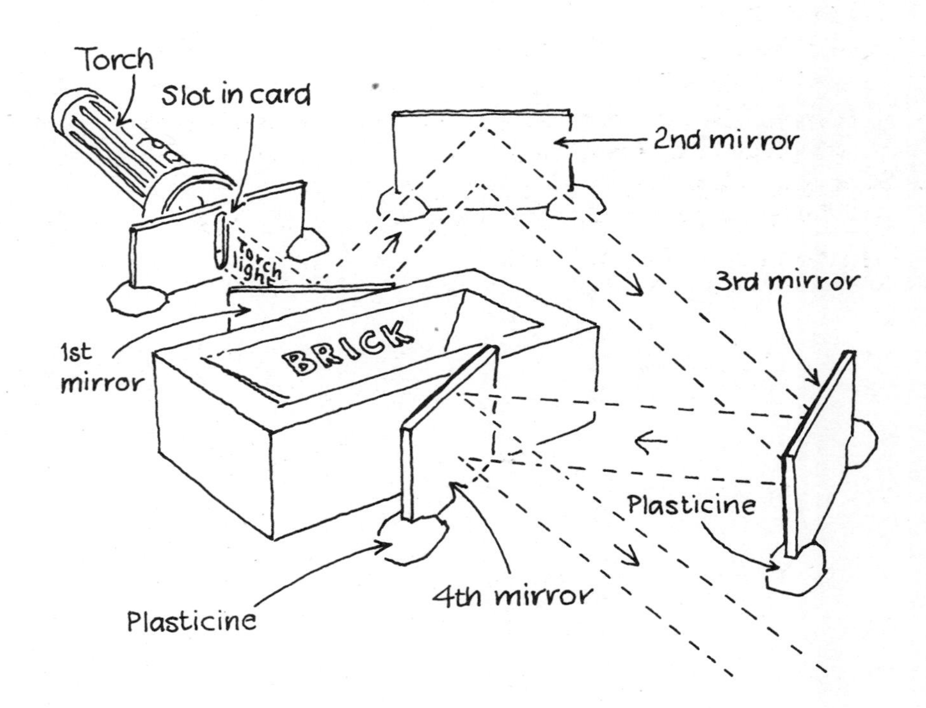

We live at the bottom of what might be called an ocean of air, which is many kilometres thick. The air presses down on everything with a pressure that is about the same as the weight of one kilogram on each square centimetre. We live constantly with this pressure, and we do not notice it.

Air is one of the most valuable resources on our planet, and one which, as a civilisation, we tend to abuse. It has many remarkable properties, some of which will be introduced to the children in this chapter.

Children will enjoy making a Legomobile and watching it move, powered by the release of pressurised air. 'Crush a can' will demonstrate the power of air, while 'Potato popper' is a fun introduction to compression. The Bernoulli effect can be seen operating in 'Amazing funnel' and 'Aerofoils'.

Sound waves

Objective
To show how revolving air, set in motion by sound waves, can put out a lighted candle.

Age range
Nine to eleven.

Group size
Pairs or small groups.

What you need
A cardboard tube (such as a cocoa container), closed at one end if possible, a pair of scissors, large balloons, candles, saucers, safety matches.

What to do
If you are unable to find tubes with covered ends, it is quite easy to adapt open-ended tubes by covering one end with a piece of thin card.

Show the children how to make a small hole (about 1½cm in diameter) in the closed end of the tube. When they have done this, they should cut a piece out of the balloon and stretch it tightly over the other end of the tube. The tightness of the balloon should be sufficient to hold it in place.

Next the children can light a candle and stand it in a saucer. Then they should hold the tube about 30cm away from the candle, with the pierced end of the tube pointing at the flame. Ask them to tap once or twice on the stretched balloon. If the tube is aimed correctly, the flame will be extinguished.

If the flame only flickers the children should try tapping a little harder. With practice they will soon be able to do it. If a larger tube is used, such as a biscuit container, the effect will work further away from the candle.

Scientific notes

When the stretched balloon is tapped, this creates a movement of air down the tube in the form of a revolving air wave. This in turn causes the air to shoot out of the hole at speed, putting out the flame.

Science AT1, 9, 10

Potato popper

Objective
To show how compressed air can force an object to travel a considerable distance.

Age range
Eight to eleven.

Group size
Pairs.

What you need
Metal tubes about 20cm long and 1½cm in diameter (available from DIY stores), small sticks or pencils, old and new potatoes (if possible), knife.

What to do
Slice the potato into pieces about 1cm thick, and ask the pairs of children to push both ends of their metal tubes into a slice of potato. Small pieces of potato will stick in the ends of the tube, blocking them.

While one child holds the tube, the other should take the stick or pencil and push on the potato at one end. If he pushes firmly and quickly enough, the piece of potato at the other end of the tube will fly off, like a bullet from a gun, making a loud 'pop' as it does so. Can the children work out what causes the pop?

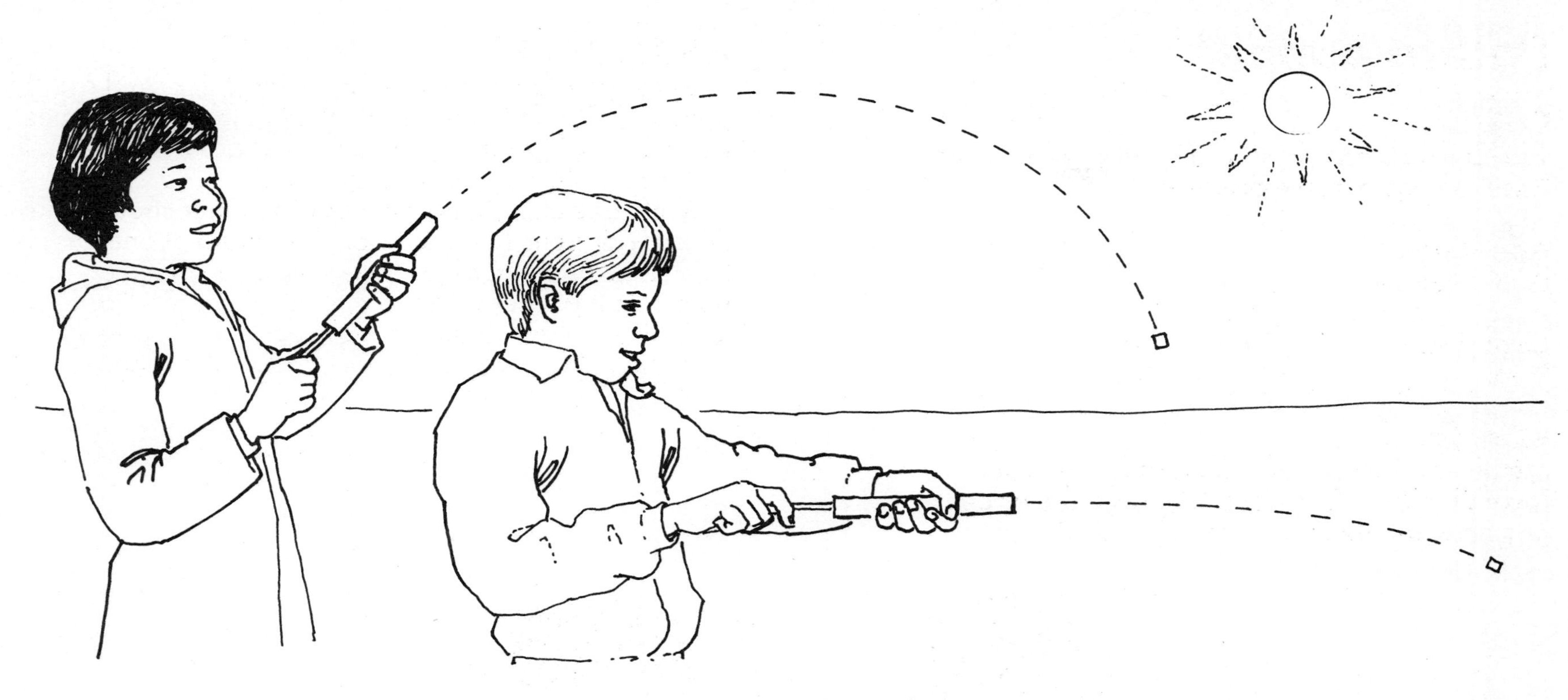

Follow-up

Ask the children to experiment and find answers to the following questions.

- Does the thickness of the slice of potato make any difference?
- Which produces the better result – a new potato or an old one?
- If the metal tube were of a different size, how would it affect the end result?
- Will the piece of potato go further if it flies off in an upward arc (parabola) or horizontally?
- Can the children invent a game with proper rules that can be played with the potato popper?

Scientific notes

When each end of the metal tube is blocked by potato, the air inside is trapped. Pushing the piece of potato with the stick causes the air inside to compress ('get squashed' for younger children). When pushed hard, the compressed air forces the piece of potato at the other end to shoot out rapidly. New potato works better. An old potato tends to get a little soggy!

The potato will go further if it is aimed upwards rather than horizontally. This can be further proved by throwing a tennis ball, or aiming water from a hose pipe in a similar fashion.

Science AT1, 9, 10

Amazing funnel

Objective
To demonstrate that moving air has less pushing power than still air.

Age range
Seven to eleven.

Group size
Individuals.

What you need
Small plastic funnels, table tennis balls (ideally with some spots marked randomly with a red felt-tipped pen), plastic straws which fit tightly in the funnel stem, playing cards (or similar sized pieces of card), cotton reels, drawing pins.

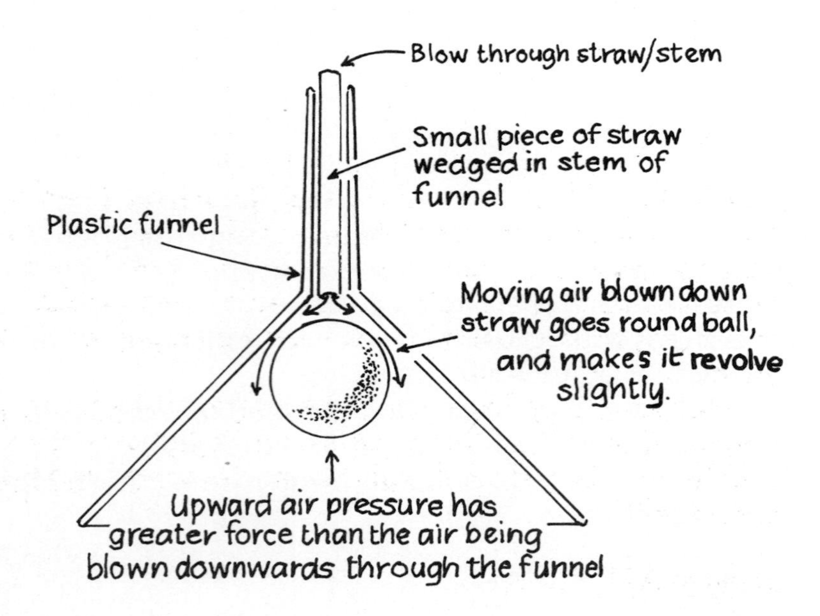

What to do
Each child should cut off a length of straw and wedge it in the stem of a funnel. Holding the funnel upside down, the children should place a table tennis ball in the base of the funnel and suck through the straw, letting go of the ball as they do so. As might be expected, the ball will remain in the funnel.

Again holding the table tennis ball in the base of the funnel, the children should blow through the straw, letting go of the ball. The ball will remain in the funnel, revolving slightly as it does so. The spots on the ball make it easier to see that it is turning.

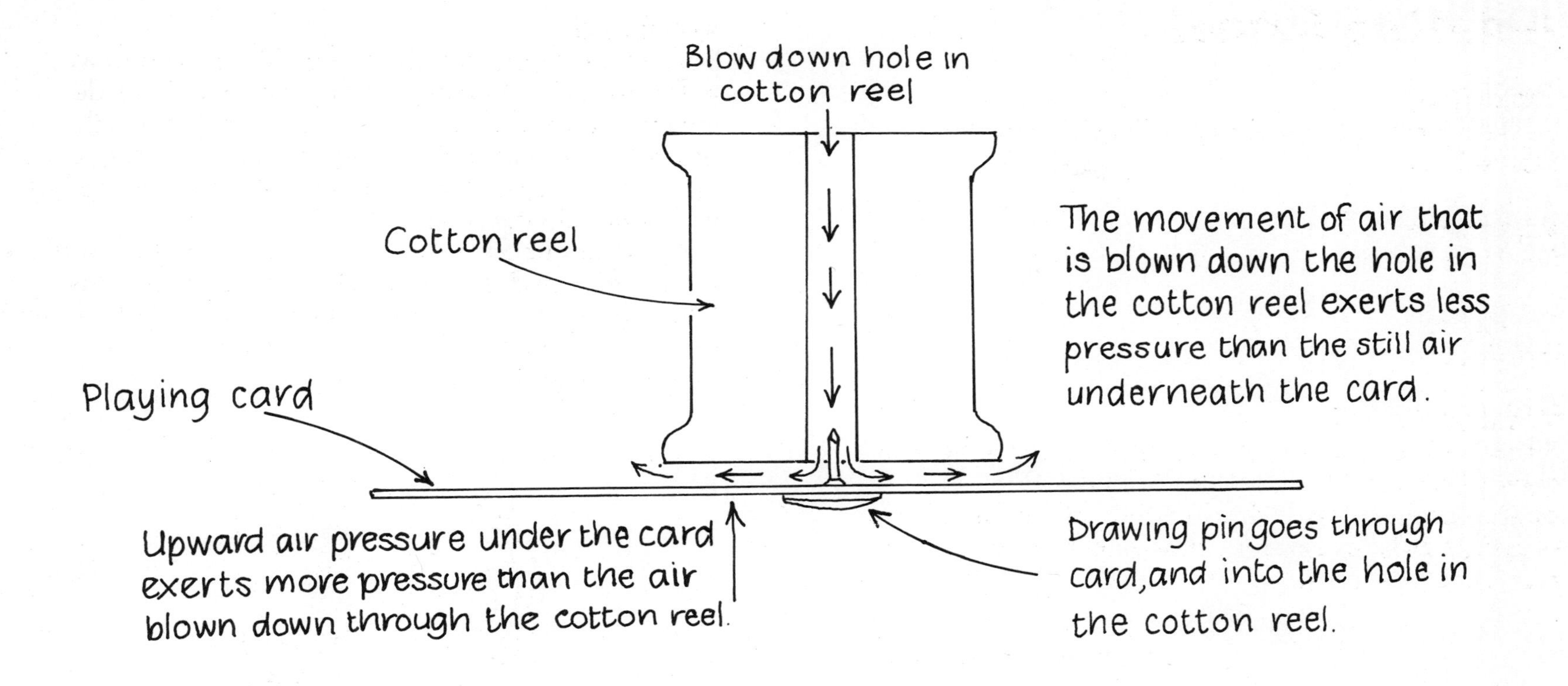

Follow-up

- Ask the children to see what happens if there is no straw in the funnel.
- The children can push a drawing pin through the centre of a playing card, and hold the card underneath a cotton reel so that the shaft of the drawing pin is in the hole. If they blow down the hole in the cotton reel, letting go of the card as they do so, the card will remain.

Scientific notes

The eighteenth-century scientist Daniel Bernoulli discovered that moving air has far less pushing power than still air. This is now known as 'the Bernoulli effect'.

In the funnel experiment the upward air pressure on the ball keeps it in the funnel. When someone blows down through the funnel, the moving air around the ball exerts less pressure than the still air which pushes upon the bottom of the ball.

In the follow-up experiment the same principle applies. The upward air pressure under the card is greater than that from the air blown down through the cotton reel.

Science AT1, 9, 10

Floating ball

Objective
To demonstrate that moving air has less pushing power than still air.

Age range
Nine to eleven.

Group size
Individuals or pairs.

What you need
Some special bendable straws, table tennis balls, hair-drier, cylindrical vacuum cleaner, beach ball.

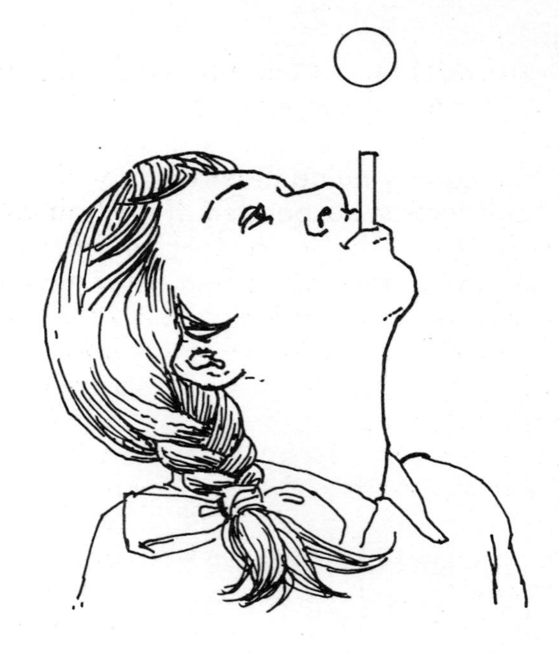

What to do
First, ask the children each to bend a straw so that the bent section is at right angles to the rest of the staw. They should then place their straws in their mouths like a pipe, ensuring that the longer part is horizontal, with the short part pointing upwards.

The table tennis ball should be held just above the short part of the straw. Instruct the children to take a very deep breath and blow through the straw *slowly* as they let go of the ball.

If this is done correctly, the ball will remain suspended in mid-air instead of falling. The secret of doing it successfully is to make sure that the straw is horizontal, forming a right angle where it bends.

If you can only obtain straight straws, let the children try using these with their heads tipped back.

Follow-up

If the children switch on a hair-drier and put a ball in the column of air that is blowing upwards, it will remain suspended.

The children can try tilting the hair-drier slightly; the ball should still remain suspended. If the hair-drier has a very powerful jet of air, it may be possible to introduce a second table tennis ball. They may then revolve around one another for a short while.

Do not let the children keep the hair-drier on too long, or the hot air will cause the celluloid table tennis ball to change shape a little!

The same effect can also be achieved with an old cylindrical vacuum cleaner. You will have to convert the vacuum cleaner's sucking action into a blowing one. To do this, remove the pipe or tubing from one end and insert it in the other end – making sure that the vacuum cleaner is empty! You can then suspend a table tennis ball or another lightweight ball such as a beach ball.

Warning: both follow-up experiments involve electricity, so adult supervision is required.

Scientific notes

The ball stays at a point where the moving air exerts less pressure than the still air around the ball. The pressure of this still air keeps it on the moving column of air.

Science AT1, 9, 10

Balloon in a teacup

Objective
To demonstrate how air pressure can lift teacups.

Age range
Eight to eleven.

Group size
Pairs or small groups.

What you need
Some old teacups, round balloons.

What to do
One of the children should partly blow up a balloon, and then her partner should press two teacups against it. Now the first child can continue blowing up the balloon until it is quite large, while the other continues to hold the two cups against the balloon. When the balloon is fully inflated, instruct the cup holder to release his hold. The cups will stay clinging to the balloon, and in fact, if the balloon is lifted up by its mouthpiece, the cups will remain as if by magic.

Follow-up
How many cups or mugs can be made to cling to the balloon? Since extra hands will be needed to hold the cups while the balloon is being inflated, the pairs could team up to make groups of four.

Scientific notes
The cups make an airtight seal with the rubber of the balloon. As the balloon is inflated, the rubber stretches, increasing the pressure inside each cup. The force generated is soon greater than that exerted by gravity, and this enables the balloon to hold up the cups.

Science AT1, 9, 10

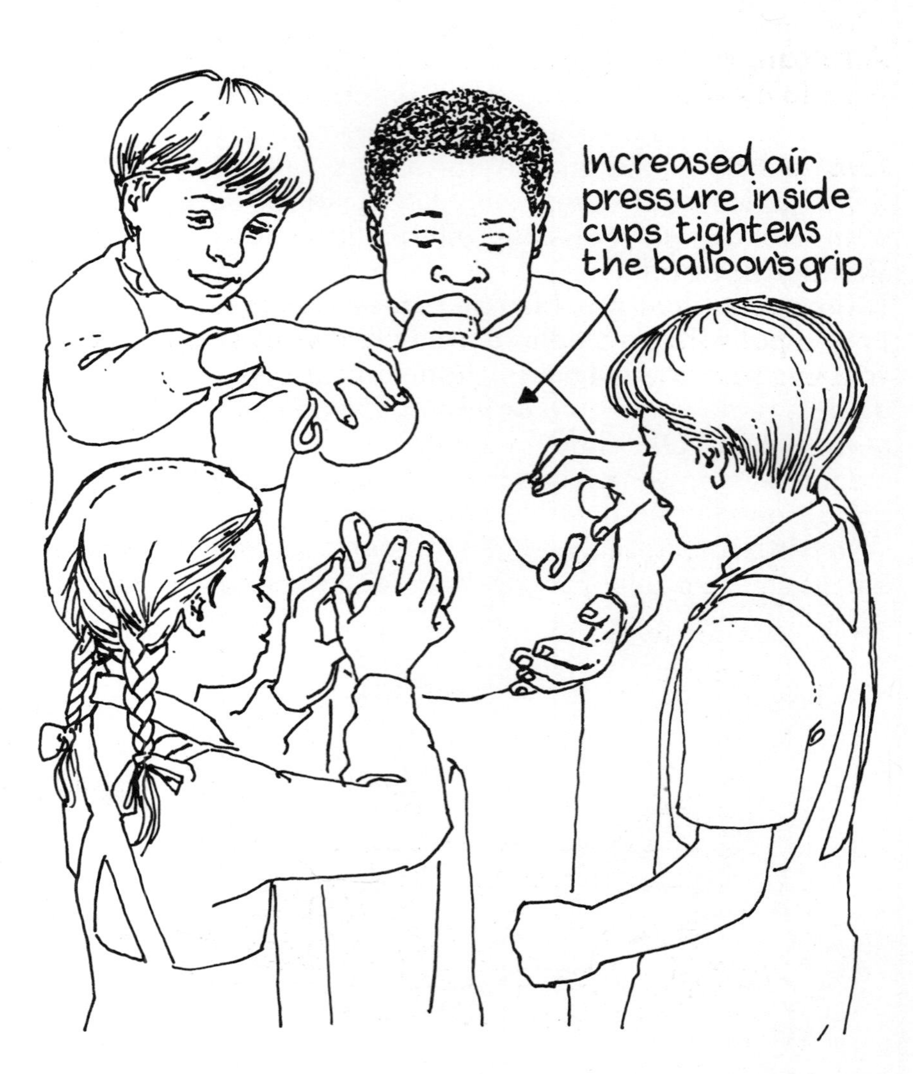

Legomobile

Objective
To demonstrate how air power can make a toy car move.

Age range
Nine to eleven.

Group size
Small groups.

What you need
Lego or other construction kits, the tops of large felt-tipped pens (for example, Berol Boardwriters), pieces of plastic straw about 4cm in length, a bradawl.

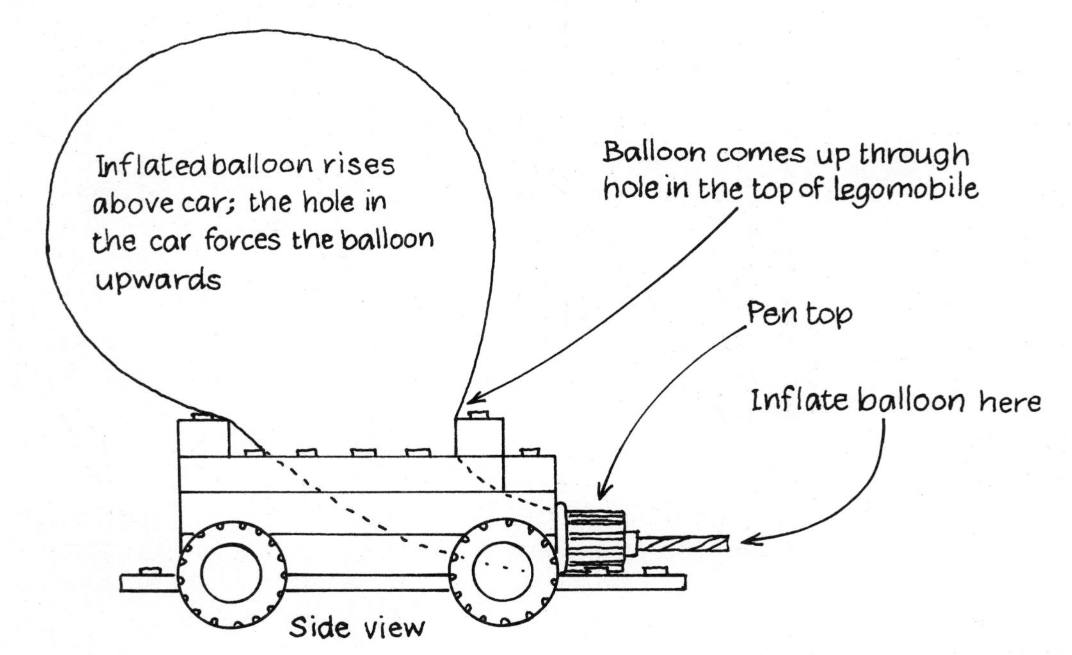

What to do
Ask each group to make a car similar to the one in the illustration, using Lego or another construction kit. The car should be made in such a way that a balloon can be attached as shown, so that it will rise above the car when inflated and not drag on the wheels. The wheels must move easily, without sticking.

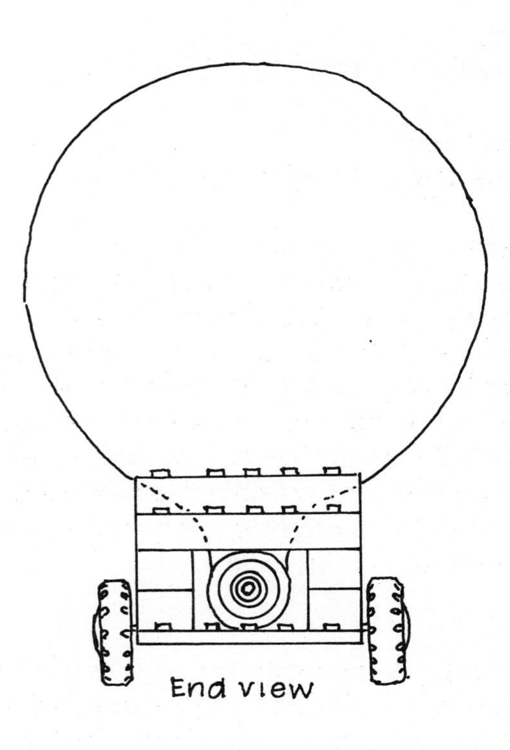

Ask the children to wash the pen tops thoroughly. When they are dry, a bradawl can be used to make a hole in the end of each top, just large enough for the end of the straw to fit inside tightly.

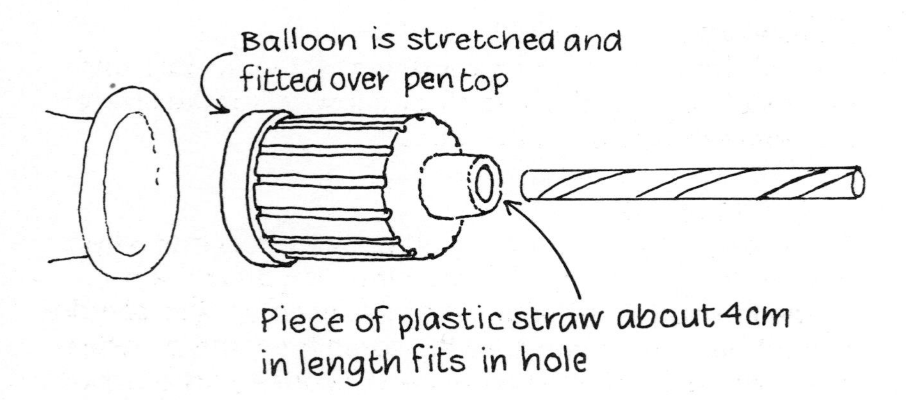

Next, the children should stretch and fit a balloon over the other end of their pen top, and fit the balloon and pen top to their car as shown. Then they can blow through the straw and inflate the balloon. Air can be prevented from escaping by putting a finger over the end of the straw.

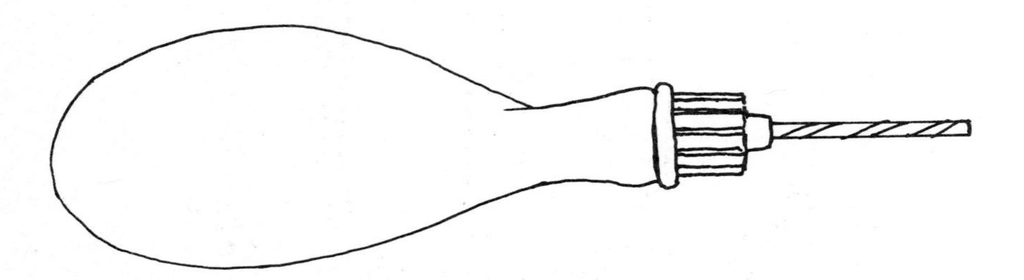

The children should place their cars on a smooth surface, and remove their fingers from the straws. Then they can watch the cars go!

Follow-up

Ask the children to experiment and find the answers to the following questions.

- Does the amount of air blown into the balloon make any difference to the distance the car travels?
- Does the size of the balloon make any difference?
- What is the best surface for the car to travel on?
- Will the car travel better if it is lighter?

Scientific notes

When a balloon is inflated there is a higher air pressure in the balloon than in the air around it. When the air in the balloon is released, the balloon shoots away in the opposite direction to the air escaping from it. The straw helps to decrease the rate at which the air is released.

When the balloon is attached to the car, the energy is harnessed to make the car travel. A similar phenomenon causes movement in a space rocket or jet engine.

Science AT1, 9, 10

Oxygen burner

Objective
To demonstrate how a burning candle uses up the oxygen in the air.

Age range
Nine to eleven.

Group size
Small groups.

What you need
Fruit dishes, jam-jars and bottles of different sizes, candles, matches.

What to do
Each group should place a fruit dish on a level surface, position a candle in the centre of the dish and light the candle carefully.

Next, they should pour some water into the dish, and very carefully place the jam-jar over the burning candle. After a few seconds, the candle flame will go out and the water will rise up inside the jam-jar.

Follow-up
The children can try this experiment with jam-jars and bottles of varying sizes, to discover whether the size of the bottle makes any difference.

Scientific notes
A simple explanation of this phenomenon is that when the candle is burning it is using the oxygen in the air inside the bottle. When most of it is used up, the candle cannot burn any longer. At the same time, the pressure of the air in the bottle is reduced because part of it has been used. Water then rises and occupies the place of the vanished oxygen.

Science AT1, 6, 9

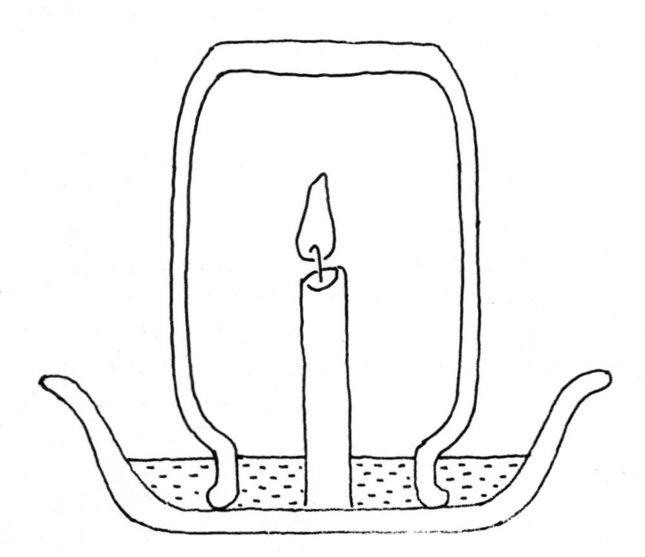

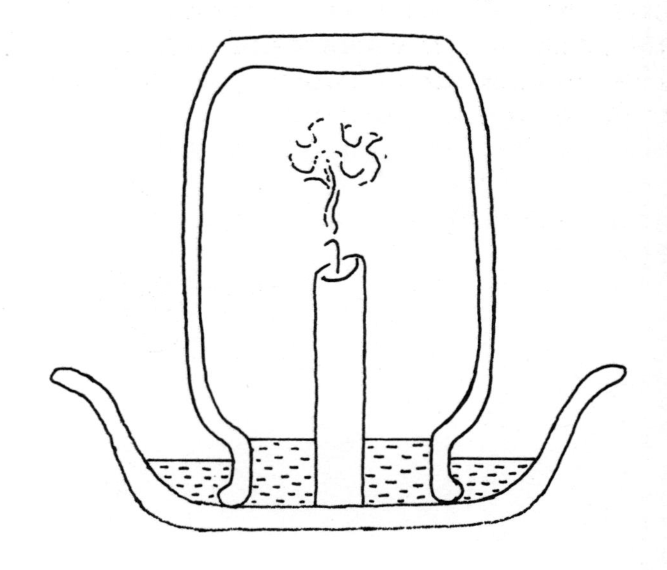

Crush a can

Objective
To demonstrate how air pressure can crush a metal oil can.

Age range
Ten to eleven.

Group size
The whole class.

What you need
A five-litre metal oil can with a screw-on cap, an electric or gas stove, a sink with a water supply, empty plastic lemonade or cola bottles.

What to do
NOTE: This experiment is dangerous and must only be carried out by an adult, at a safe distance from the children.

Wash out the oil can, making sure it is thoroughly clean. Pour several cups of water into it.

Place the can on the stove and bring the water to the boil. Allow it to boil for a short while with the steam coming out of the top.

Replace the top. **Be careful, as the can will now be very hot.**

Put the oil can in a sink under a tap of cold running water. The metal can will crumple and collapse under the weight of atmospheric pressure.

Follow-up

Here is a similar experiment which can be tried by the children. They should fill a plastic lemonade bottle with water. One child should hold the bottle with one hand on the bottom and the other over the top, and turn it upside down. If he removes his hand from the mouth of the bottle, *instantly replacing it*, some of the water will escape and part of the bottle should cave in.

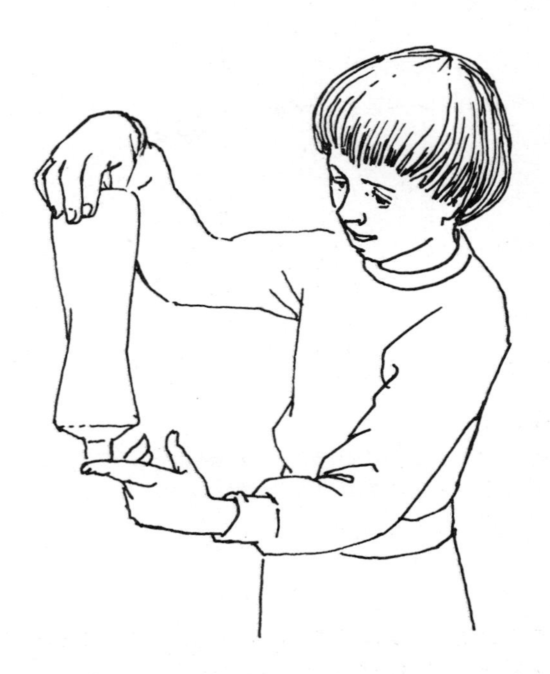

Scientific notes

When the can of water boils, the escaping steam will force out most of the air. With the cap replaced, the steam will condense back to water. This will result in a much lower air pressure inside the can. The greater air pressure outside will make the can collapse.

In the second experiment a similar principle applies. When the hand covering the opening is removed, a small amount of water escapes. However, if the hand is replaced instantly, air cannot get inside to replace the water. The result is a slightly reduced air pressure in the bottle. The greater pressure outside will then cause a thin plastic bottle to cave in slightly.

Science AT1, 9, 10

Aerofoils

Objective
To demonstrate how an aerofoil such as an aeroplane wing works.

Age range
Nine to eleven.

Group size
Pairs.

What you need
Pieces of card approximately 10cm by 24cm, plastic straws, adhesive, scissors, thin string cut into two-metre lengths, hair-drier.

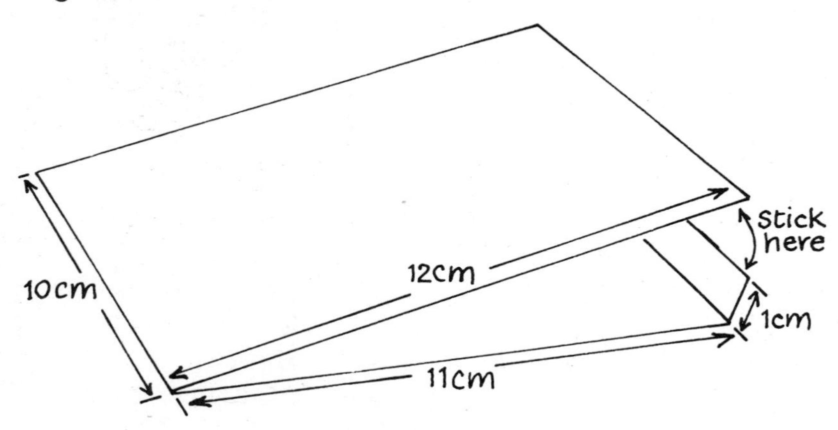

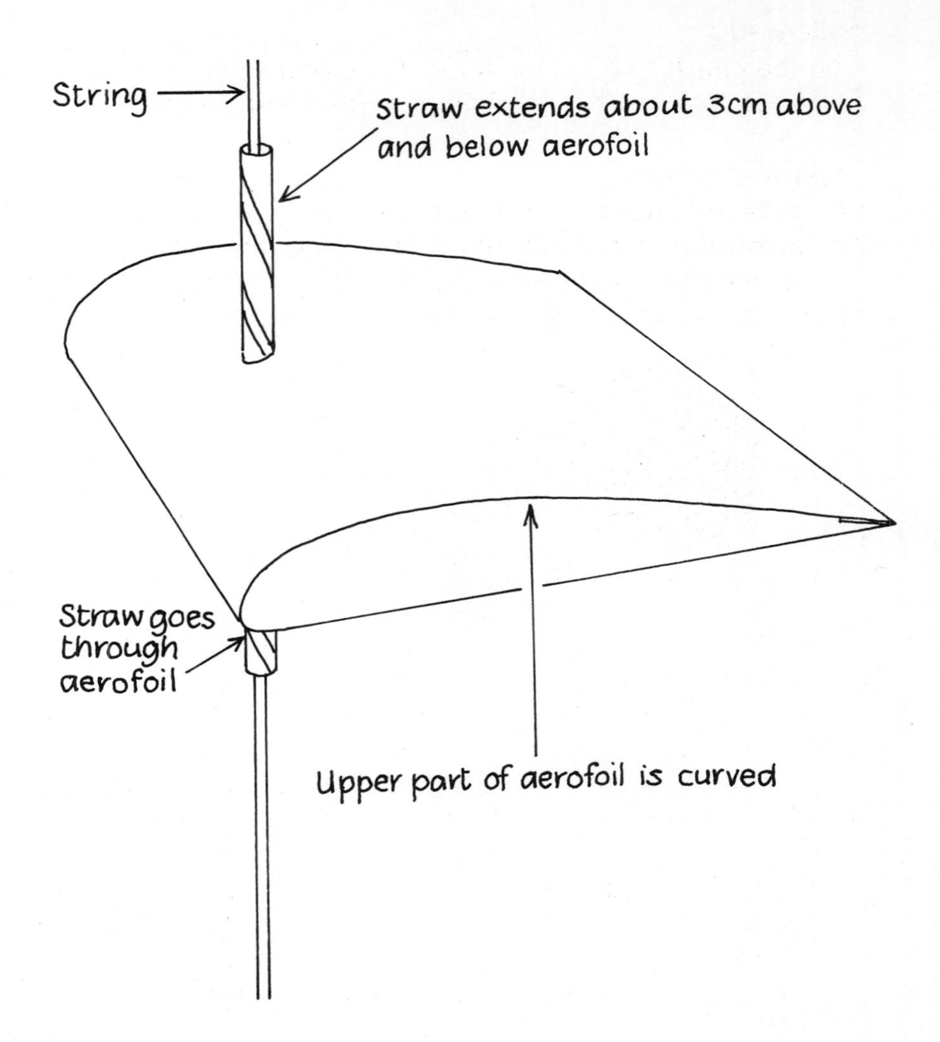

What to do
Each pair should make an aerofoil as shown, and take turns to use the hair-drier. One of the children should hold each end of the string, keeping it vertical and taut, with the aerofoil at the bottom. The other child can then hold the hair-drier level with it, and switch it on.

Keeping the hair-drier about 10cm away from the aerofoil, the child should slowly move it upwards. The aerofoil should now move up the string at the same rate as the hair-drier. It is important to keep the hair-drier level with the aerofoil all the time, as otherwise the aerofoil will fall back down the string.

Follow-up

Can the children guess what will happen if a tail fin is added to the aerofoil? Let them experiment to find out.

Scientific notes

Wings have a special shape, called an 'aerofoil'. When the aerofoil is at the bottom of the string, the air pressure above and below it is the same. When the hair-drier is switched on, the air flows quickly past the aerofoil. Because the top part of the aerofoil is curved, the air moves faster over it.

The Swiss scientist Bernoulli discovered that when air moves faster it has lower pressure. The air pressure on top of the wing is less than the air pressure underneath. The result is 'lift'; the wing rises.

Aerofoils only work when air flows past them quickly. This is why an aircraft has to speed down the runway before it takes off. Once it is moving very fast, there is enough lift to raise the plane into the sky.

Science AT1, 9, 10

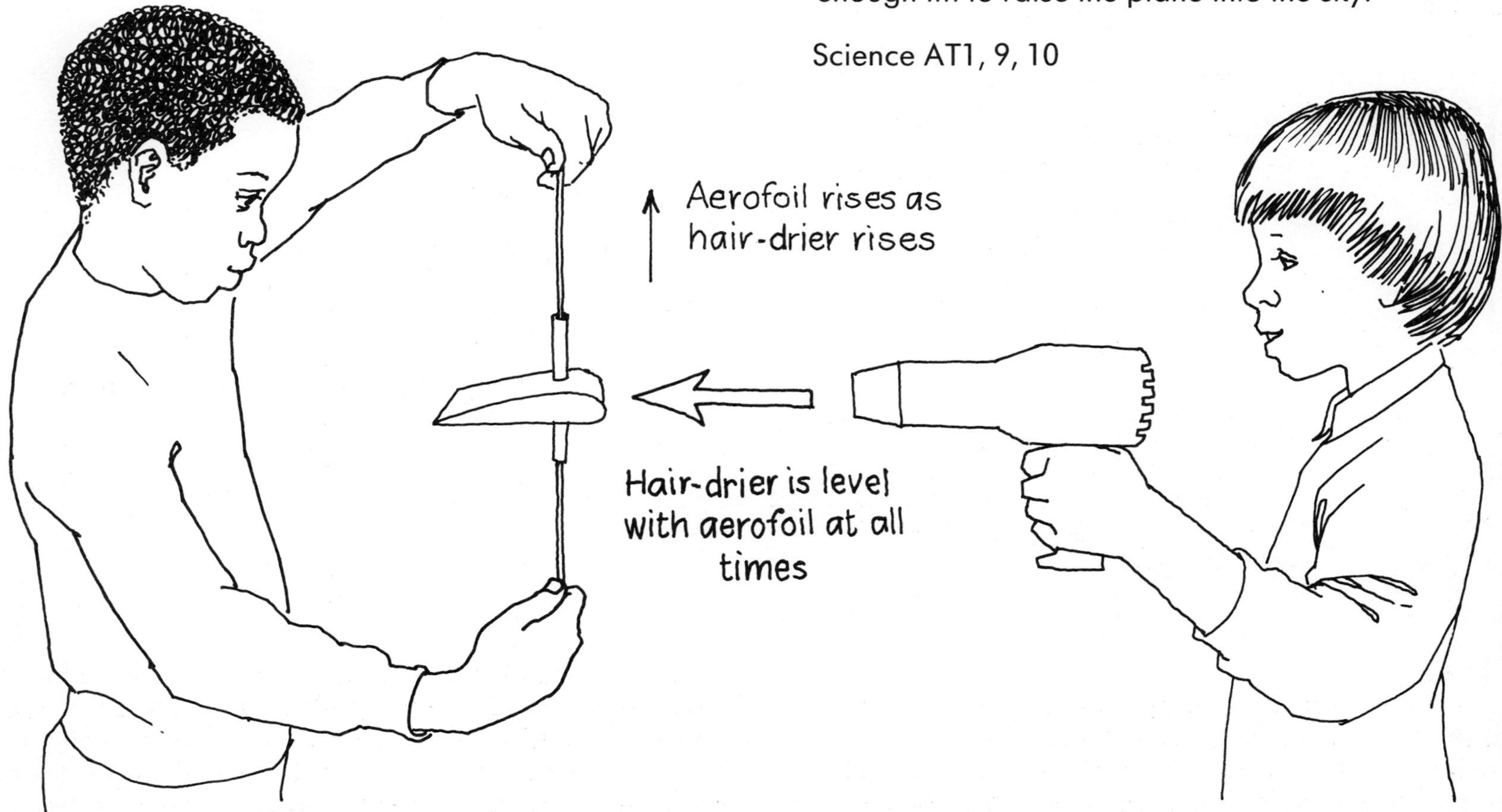

Drop a card

Objective
To demonstrate how air will affect cards in different ways as they fall.

Age range
Nine to eleven.

Group size
Large groups.

What you need
A pack of playing cards, small empty plastic buckets or similar containers.

What to do
Each group should place their bucket on the floor, and the first child should hold a playing card at about shoulder level above it. The card should be held vertically, pointing downwards.

The child should then drop the card and try to get it to land in the bucket. An occasional card may land in the bucket, but most of them will spin away from it.

The next child should hold his card horizontally, again at shoulder level. The card should float gently downwards and land in the bucket.

Follow-up

Another child can hold the card at waist level. With an outward flick of the wrist, she should release the card. This may take a bit of practice in order to get the knack, but if it is done correctly the card will skim through the air. *There is no arm movement, just wrist action.*

Scientific notes

When the card is held pointing downwards and released, the air forces the card into a downward spin. It will usually spin away from the bucket. When the card is held flat, the air offers resistance much as it does when a parachute falls. The card therefore floats down and should land in the bucket.

In the experiment described in the follow-up, the card skims through the air because there is very little air resistance.

Science AT1, 9, 10

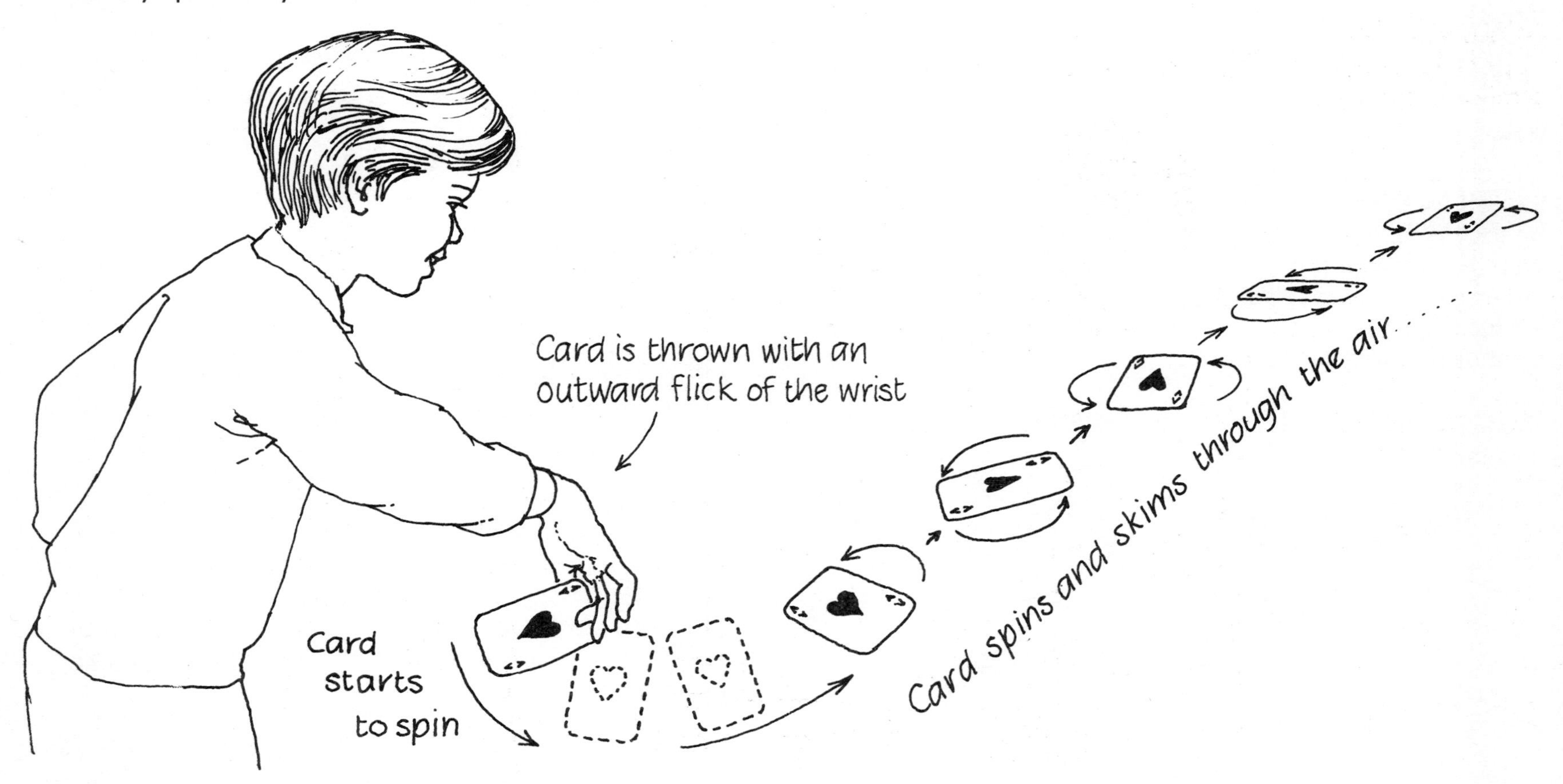

Flick it

Objective
A simple demonstration of inertia.

Age range
Eight to eleven.

Group size
Individuals or pairs.

What you need
Playing cards, ten pence coins, tumblers, strips of paper about 10cm long.

What to do
The children should balance a playing card on the tip of the left forefinger and carefully place a ten pence coin on top. With the right forefinger the children should then flick the edge of the card. The card should fly off, leaving the coin still balanced on the fingertip.

This trick may require some practice, and the playing card used should be straight.

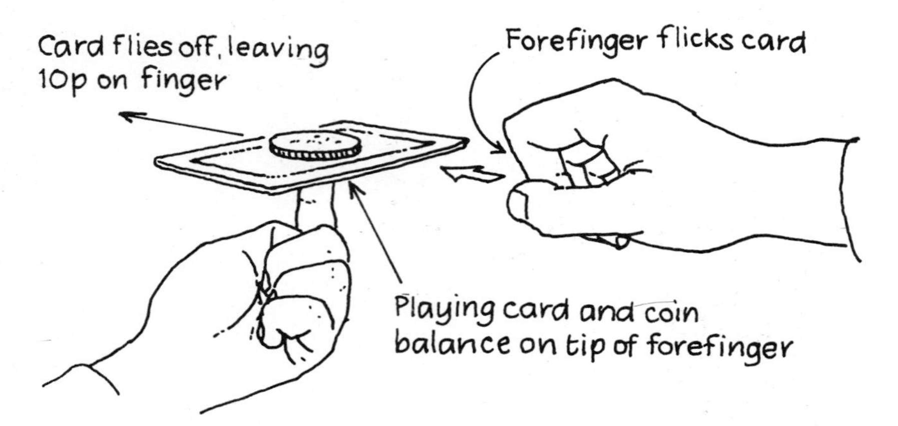

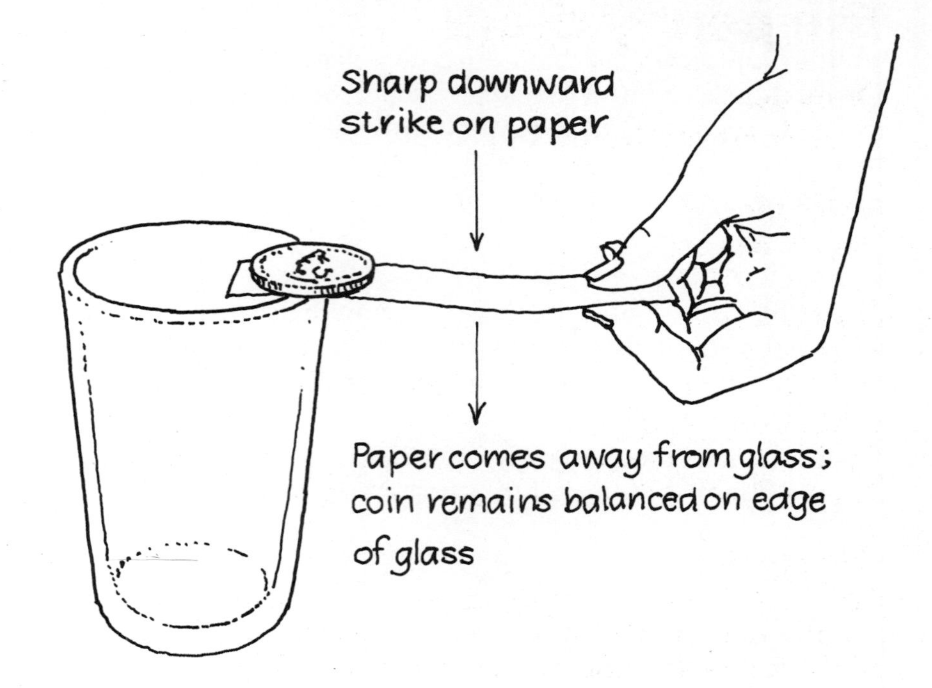

Follow-up
A coin should be balanced on a strip of paper on the edge of a tumbler, as shown. If the centre of the strip of paper is given a sharp downward tap, this will remove the paper from the glass but leave the coin balanced.

Scientific notes
Inertia is the property of a body which opposes any change in its motion. The inertia of the coin prevents its movement in both cases. The coin's weight holds it in place on the finger as the playing card is flicked away. The same applies when the strip of paper is quickly removed from the tumbler.

Science AT1, 10

The penny drops

Objective
To demonstrate the law of inertia.

Age range
Nine to eleven.

Group size
Pairs or group.

What you need
Tumblers, small coins, pencils, lengths of thin card about 3cm by 30cm, with the ends fastened to form a loop.

What to do
Place the circular piece of card on the mouth of the tumbler and put the coin on top, as illustrated. Place the pencil *inside* the loop and hit the inside of the loop, taking it sideways and away from the tumbler. The sudden removal of the loop leaves the coin in mid air, and due to inertia it drops into the glass.

Follow-up
- Ask the children to find out what happens if they hit the outside of the loop with the pencil.
- Ask them to experiment with loops of different sizes and thicknesses, with objects of various weights.

Scientific notes
The inertia of the coin prevents it from moving sideways when the paper ring is flicked away, so that it falls straight down into the glass.

Science AT1, 10

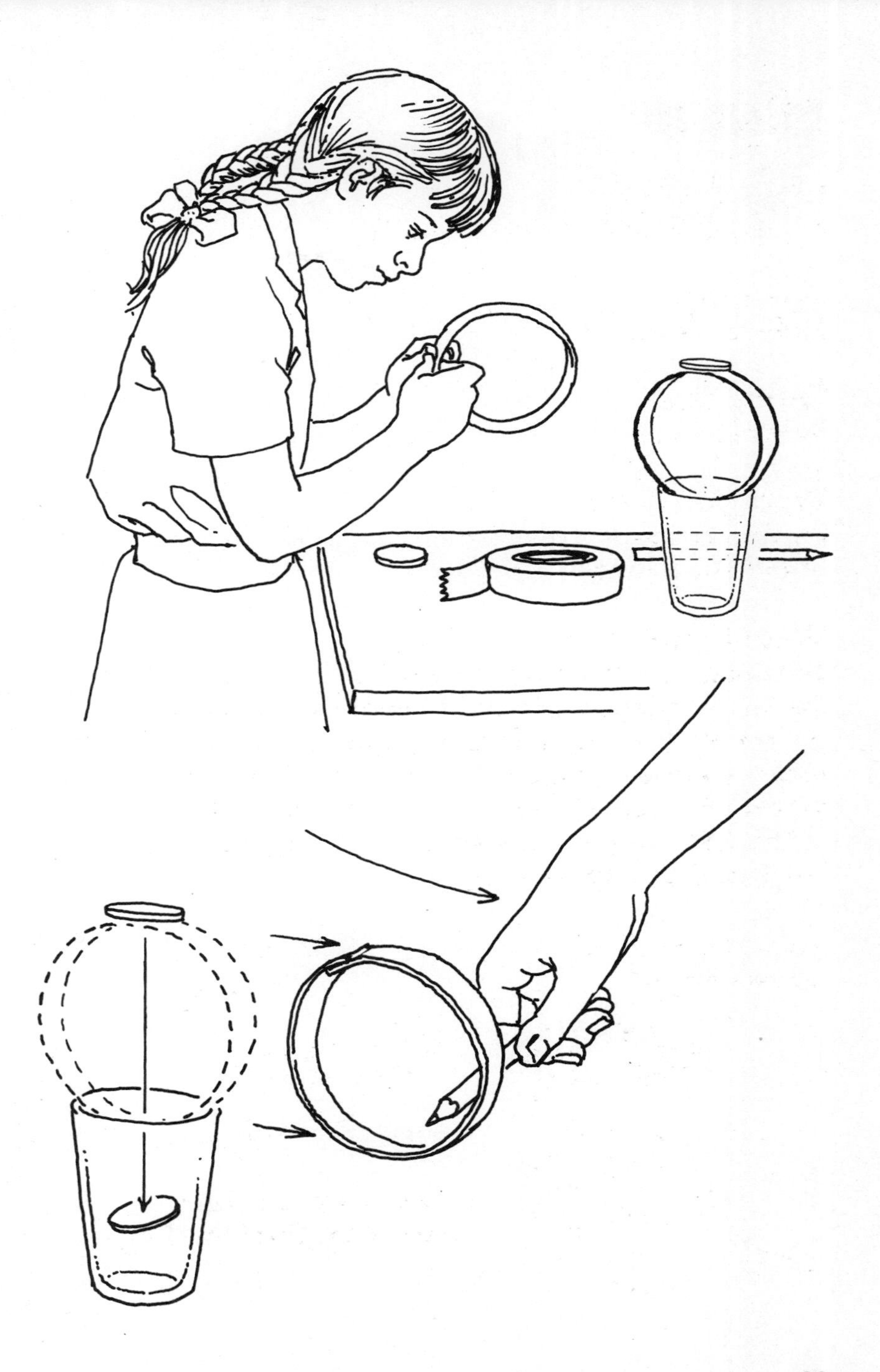

Water

Water covers about two-thirds of the Earth's surface, and life could not exist without it.

Water can exist in three forms. Usually it is seen in liquid form as it flows out of a tap or fills our rivers and lakes. However, it can freeze until it becomes a solid – snow or ice – or it can be heated until it boils and escapes into the air as a gas – water vapour.

Children usually love working with water, and the experiments in this section will enable them to learn about some of its properties. However, beware! Sometimes children and water do not coexist peacefully. Make sure the experiments are carried out in an appropriate place – in the sink, on the draining board, or outside.

Tricky bottle

Objective
To show how air pressure can prevent water from pouring out of a hole.

Age range
Five to eleven.

Group size
Individuals or pairs.

What you need
Plastic soft drinks bottles, knitting needles.

What to do
Help the children to make a small hole in the middle of their bottle. Care must be taken when doing this; you could do it in advance for younger children.

Ask the children to put a finger over the hole and fill the bottle with water. When the bottle is full, they should put the top on. They will see that the water does not come out of the hole. Next, ask them to loosen the bottle top. Water will now flow out of the hole. If they tighten the bottle top, the flow will cease.

Follow-up
Ask the children to think about the following questions and experiment to find answers.

- If there were two holes in the bottle, would the water flow out?
- How big can the hole be before the water automatically flows out of the bottle, whether the top is on or not?

• If the hole is near the bottom of the bottle, does it make a difference to the distance the water shoots out?

Scientific notes

When the cap is on the bottle, the water is kept inside by the pressure of the air pushing on the hole, and to a lesser extent by the surface tension across the hole. With a small hole, surface tension acts like a thin sheet of rubber to keep the water inside the bottle. The two forces of air pressure and surface tension together are greater than the force exerted by gravity, which would otherwise make the water leak out.

When the cap is removed, air pressure acts on the water from the top of the bottle. This pressure is equal to the pressure pushing on the hole, and the two pressures cancel each other out, so there is nothing to prevent the water from flowing out under the force of gravity.

Science AT1, 10

Bottled tornado

Objective

To create the vortex of a tornado or a whirlpool within a bottle.

Age range

Eight to eleven.

Group size

Pairs or small groups.

What you need

Clear plastic cola or lemonade bottles with tops, some very strong adhesive that will stick metal to metal, a drill.

What to do

Drill a hole in each of the bottle tops and, with very strong adhesive, stick them together. Ask the children to get two bottles, and to fill one of them about two-thirds full of water. They should screw on one of the two bottle tops (now stuck together), and screw the other empty bottle on to the second top (see illustration).

The next stage is to turn the bottles upside down so that the bottle containing the water is at the top, and give them a gentle, circular shake. The water will pass from the top bottle to the bottom one, creating a vortex like a whirpool or a tornado as it does so. As the water enters the lower bottle it creates a shower effect.

Follow-up

- If the children cut some straws into very small pieces and place them in the bottle of water, a pretty effect occurs as the water passes from one bottle to the other.
- Before filling the bottle with water the children could put a teaspoon of powder paint in each of the bottles; for example, blue in one, yellow in the other. They should then assemble the various parts as before. As the water travels from one bottle to the other, a colour change occurs; in this instance, to green.
- If the bottles are placed on a table with the bottle containing the water at the top, after a few seconds the water will stop coming through the hole in the bottle tops. This is because the air pressure in the bottom bottle is strong enough to prevent this happening. The flow of water only starts when the bottles are shaken in circular motion.

An American company, Burnham Associates Inc., has produced a 'Tornado Tube' which replaces the bottle tops and makes the experiment easier. It is available from the Exploratory Hands On Science Centre, Bristol Old Station, Temple Meads, Bristol.

Scientific notes

As the bottles are shaken in a circular motion and the water passes through the small hole, a vortex like that ot a whirlpool or a tornado naturally occurs.

Science AT1, 9, 10

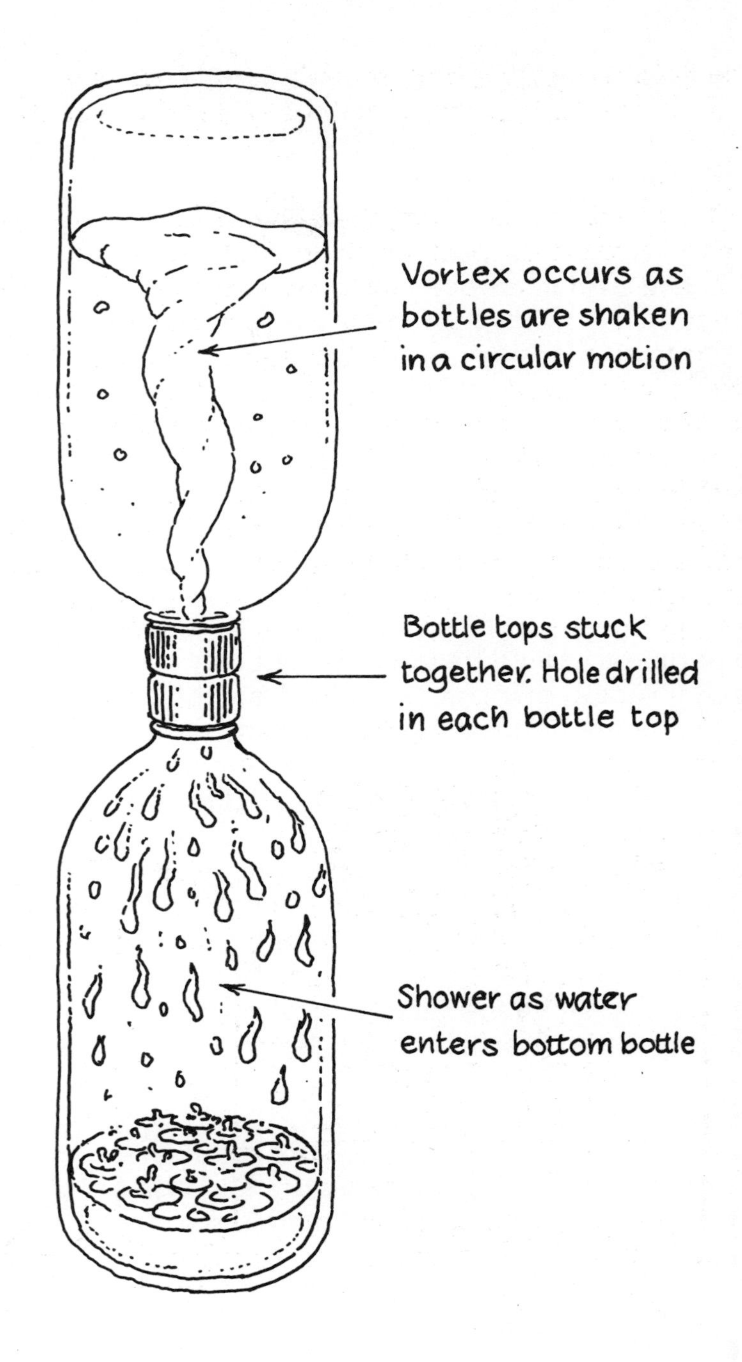

On the boil

Objective
To show how it is possible to boil water in a paper cup.

Age range
Nine to eleven.

Group size
Group or class.

What you need
Two paper cups, water, a candle, matches, dry salt, a saucer.

What to do
This experiment should be done as a demonstration, by the teacher alone, at a safe distance from the children. It demonstrates the effectiveness of water in conducting heat, but the heat source is potentially dangerous, and so the children should **never** be allowed to carry out the experiment themselves.

Put some water in the paper cup. Light the candle and put it in the saucer, and then hold the paper cup over the flame. After a short while, the water will start to boil without the paper cup getting burned.

Put some dry salt in the second cup and hold it over the flame. After a short while the cup will burn.

Follow-up
Try this experiment using other substances such as sugar, washing powder, lemonade or milk. Instead of using a paper cup, you may wish to make a paper container.

Scientific notes
In the first experiment, the water takes away the heat of the flame from the paper. The paper never gets hotter than 100°C, which is the boiling point of water. The burning point of paper is higher than this.

In the second experiment, the salt does not conduct the heat away from the paper. Salt has a melting point of 800°C, much higher than the burning point of paper. The paper reaches its burning point and catches alight.

Science AT1, 8, 13

Watering your plants

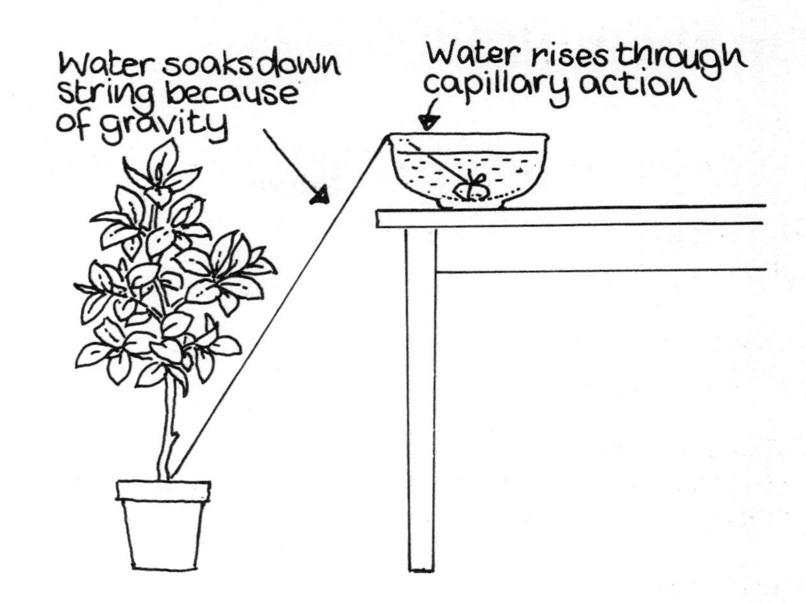

Objective
To show how it is possible to water a plant with the help of gravity and capillary action.

Age range
Eight to eleven.

Group size
Individuals, pairs or the whole class.

What you need
For each group: a table, a washing-up bowl of cold water, a stone or heavy weight, a long piece of string, a plant in a plant pot.

What to do
The bowl of water should be placed on the edge of the table. Next, the children should wet the string, put one end of it into the water, and place a stone or weight on the end of the string so that it remains in the bowl.

The plant pot should then be placed on the floor or at a lower level than the table, and the other end of the string can be attached to the base of the plant. The string should be taut.

Over a period of hours and days, water will rise up the string from the bowl, and will then soak down the string and into the plant pot. This slow continuous flow of water will keep the plant watered. It is possible to have a number of plant pots set up in this way from the same bowl of water.

Because the action in this experiment is very slow, a check on the level of water in the bowl could be undertaken on a half-daily basis. Remind the children to consider whether any water escapes by evaporation. A check could also be kept on the moistness of the soil in the plant pot.

Scientific notes
Capillary action draws water up through the air spaces between the fibres in the string. This happens because the molecules in the water are more attracted to the molecules of the string than they are to each other, and therefore they try to move away from each other and up the string. The smaller the width of a tube or air space, the further upwards the water can move.

Once the water has soaked up the string as far as the lip of the bowl, it carries on moving down the string and into the plant pot under the force of gravity.

Science AT1, 3, 10

Colour-changing plants

Objective
To demonstrate how flowers and plants suck up water by capillary action to feed their leaves and petals.

Age range
Seven to eleven.

Group size
Pairs or the whole class.

What you need
For each group: two glasses of clear water, red and blue food colouring or ink, a white carnation, a knife.

What to do
Ask the children to place some red food colouring in one glass of water, and blue in the other. Supervise them while they split the stem of the carnation with the knife and place one half of the stem in the glass of red water, and the other half in the glass of blue water.

The flower should then be left, and checked periodically for changes. After a few hours the white carnation will change colour, one half becoming red and the other blue.

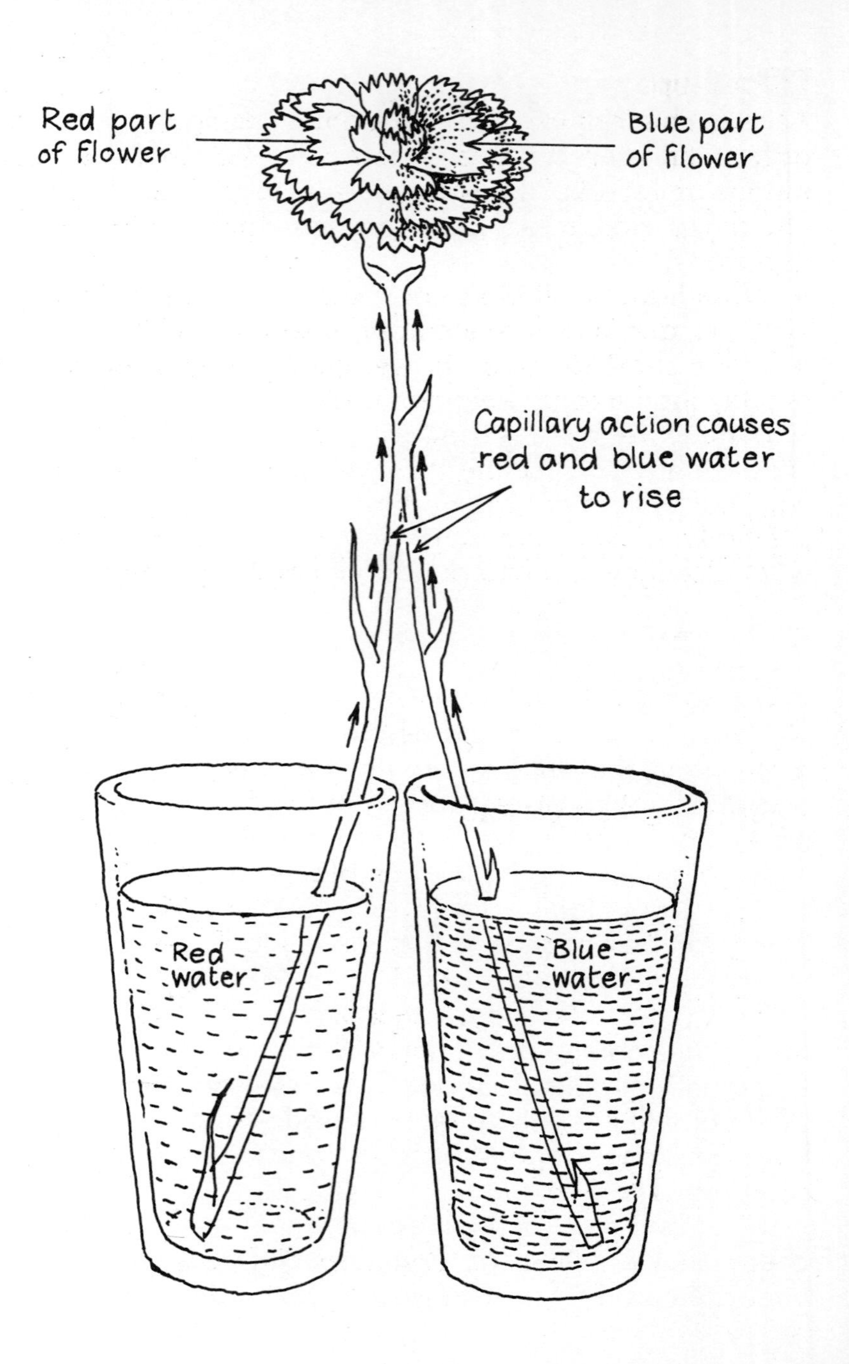

Follow-up

Ask the children to try the experiment using a number of different flowers, and vegetables such as celery, turnips, onions or carrots. Plants with leaves work best. They could experiment to find the answers to the following questions.

- What happens if the stem is split into three or four sections, and a different colour used for each?
- Will a short-stemmed flower change colour more quickly than a long-stemmed one?
- If the experiment is tried with celery, show the children how to slice the stalk lengthways to reveal the vascular system or pipe pattern.

Finally, let the children do some research and see what else they can find out about capillary action.

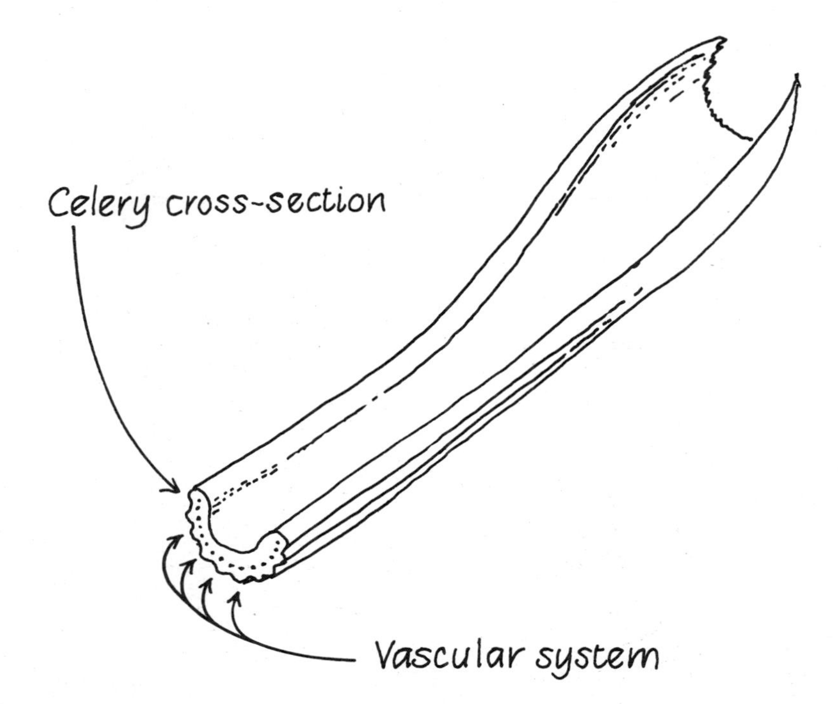

Scientific notes

The coloured water moves up the stem of the plant through narrow capillary tubes. This capillary action is made more apparent by using dyes to colour the water.

Once the red water enters the capillary tube it will not mix with the blue water, but rises up to a specific section of the flower and colours that section.

Science AT1, 3

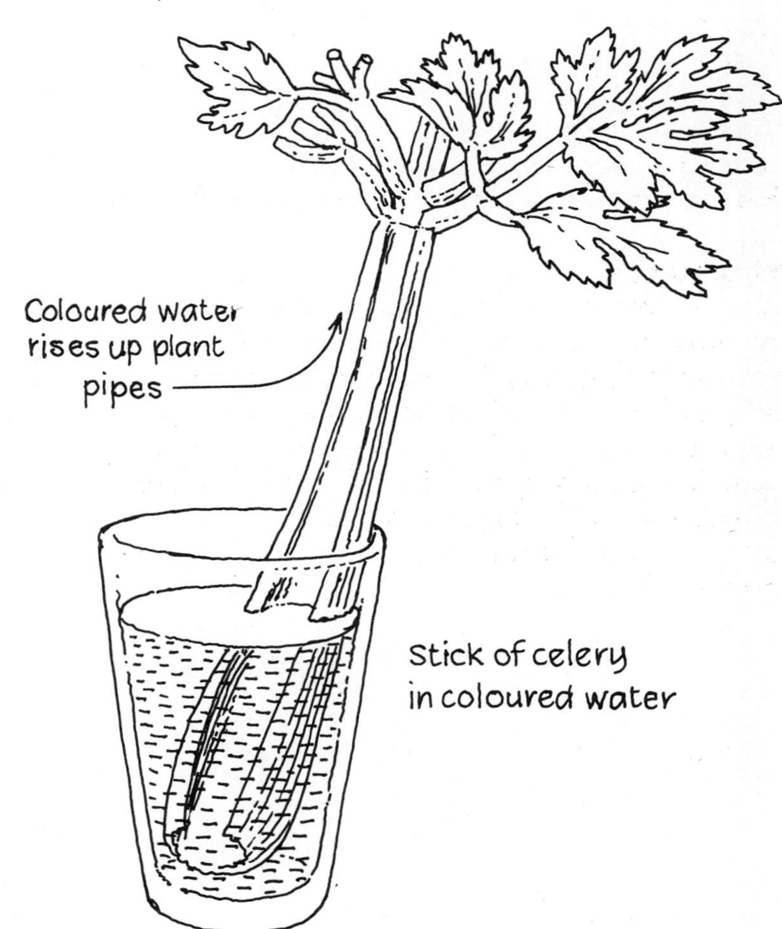

Walking water 1

Objective
To observe surface tension.

Age range
Eight to eleven.

Group size
Individuals or pairs.

What you need
Small jugs of water, pieces of string about a metre in length, small tumblers, petroleum jelly.

What to do
First the children should tie one end of the string to the handle of the jug. The other end of the string should be held to the edge of the tumbler, and the children should hold the jug, string and tumbler as shown.

They will see that the water travels along the underside of the string and into the glass. *It is essential that the string is kept taut the whole time.* If it is allowed to become too slack, the water will run off the string.

Follow-up
Let the children experiment to see what happens if the string is coated with petroleum jelly.

Scientific notes
When water flows from a tap in a steady stream it has the shape of a smooth tube, held in place by surface tension, which can be thought of as a thin, elastic membrane. In the experiment, the water molecules are attracted to the string because of surface tension.

Science AT1, 6

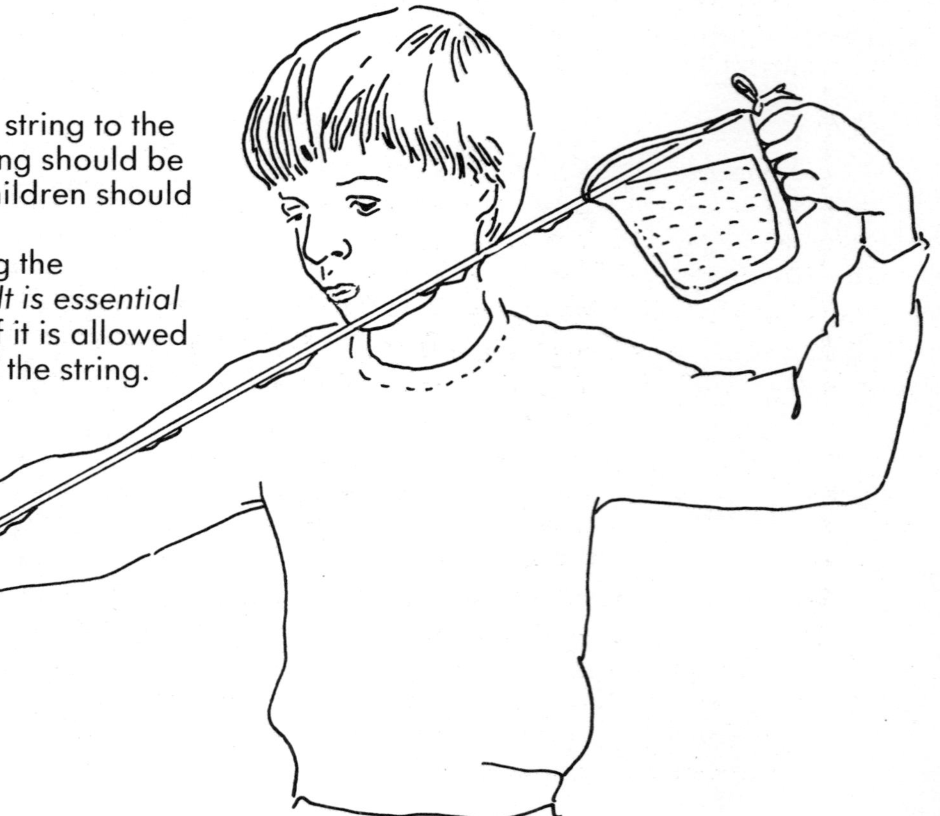

Walking water 2

Objective
To observe surface tension.

Age range
Eight to eleven.

Group size
Small groups or pairs.

What you need
Jugs of water, washing-up bowls, broom handles or similar pieces of thick dowelling made of wood and other materials, petroleum jelly.

What to do
The washing-up bowl should be placed on the floor, and one end of the wooden broom handle held above the edge of the bowl so that the upper end is at least 30cm higher than the lower end.

Water should now be poured slowly from the jug on to the upper end of the handle. Water will flow down and along the underside of the handle, and into the bowl.

Follow-up
- Ask the chldren to try this experiment with poles or handles of metal or plastic to see whether it still works.
- Can they predict what will happen if the wooden handle is coated with petroleum jelly or a similar substance?
- You could describe how, many years ago in the countryside, some people used this method to collect rain water from the eaves of their cottages. Water would flow along the underside of the protruding poles and into a water butt.

Scientific notes
Just as in 'Walking water 1', the water molecules are attracted to the wood, and the elastic skin of the water holds it to the underside of the wooden handle.

If the handle is covered in petroleum jelly as suggested in the follow-up, it becomes a surface to which water is not attracted – it will simply fall off the handle.

Science AT1, 6

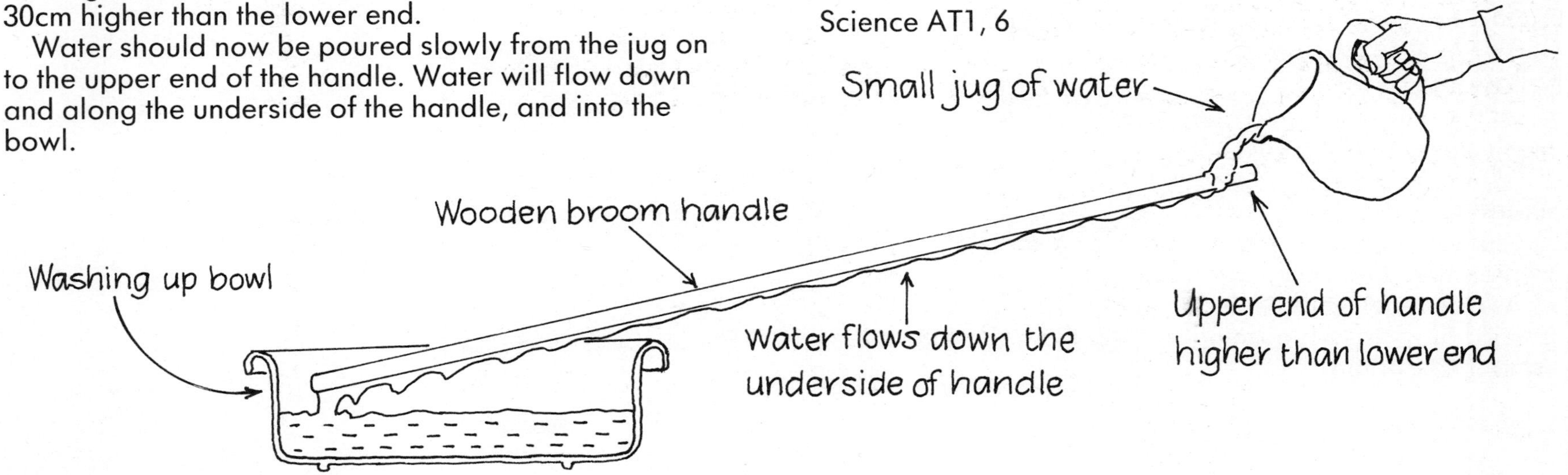

Amazing tea strainer

Objective
To show how a tea strainer (despite its holes) can support a volume of water.

Age range
Seven to eleven.

Group size
Individuals or pairs.

What you need
Milk bottles full of water, tea strainers and sieves with holes of varying sizes.

What to do
Ask the children to place the tea strainer over the top of the bottle of water, and very carefully to turn everything upside down, pressing the tea strainer against the top of the bottle all the time. A few drops of water may be lost, but most of the water will remain in the bottle.

Follow-up
- Let the children repeat the experiment with sieves and tea strainers of different sizes.

Scientific notes
The combination of surface tension and air pressure is greater than the downward force of the water. A 'skin' forms over each small hole in the tea strainer, and the upward air pressure pushing against the holes keeps the water in the bottle.

Science AT1, 10

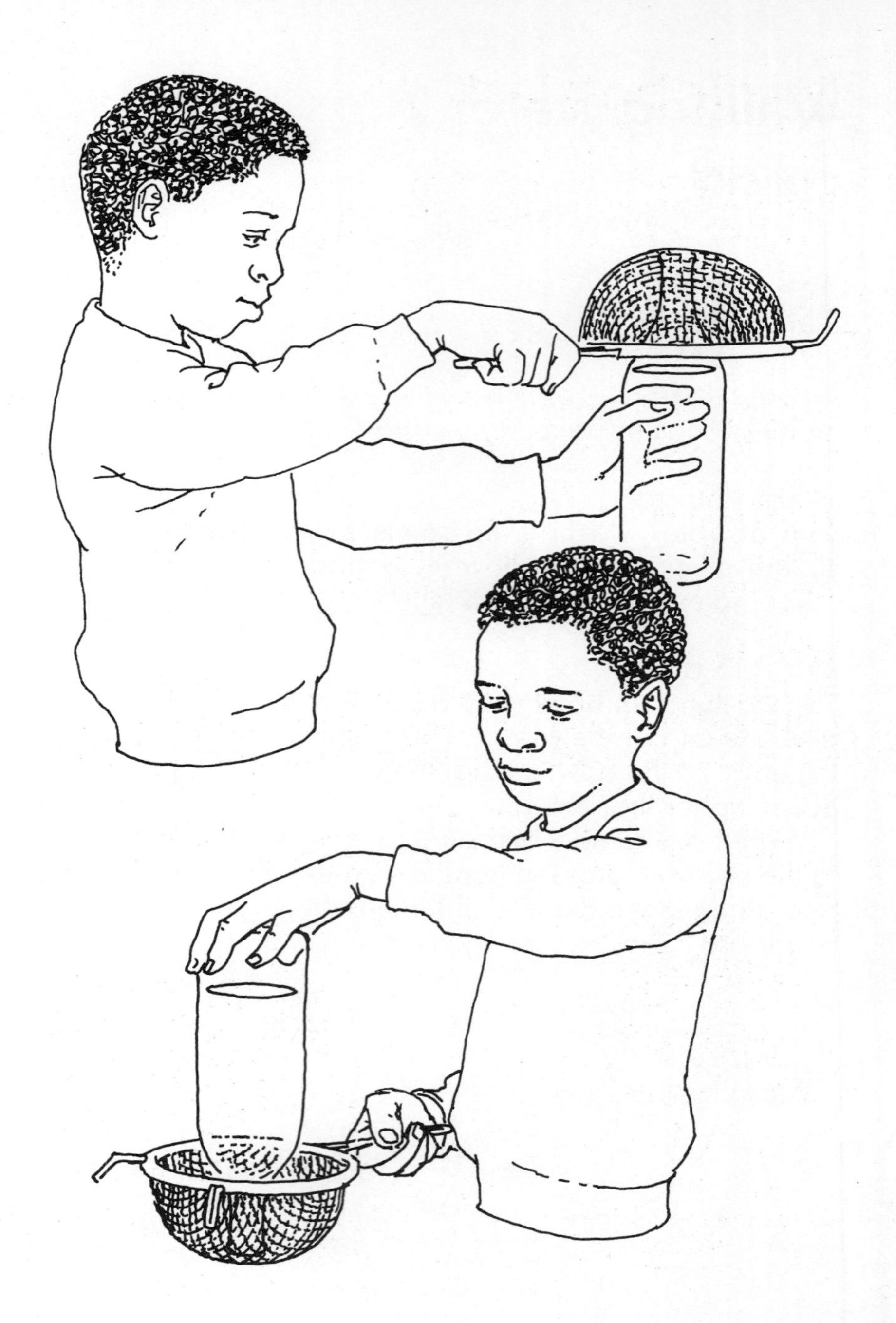

Magic bottle 1

Objective
To show that a piece of gauze (despite its holes) will prevent water from flowing out of a bottle.

Age range
Eight to eleven.

Group size
Individuals or pairs.

What you need
Cola or lemonade bottles, small pieces of wire gauze, thin wire, elastic bands, cocktail sticks.

What to do
First of all ask the children to cover the mouth of the bottle with wire gauze and secure it with a thin piece of wire or an elastic band wrapped round the bottle neck.

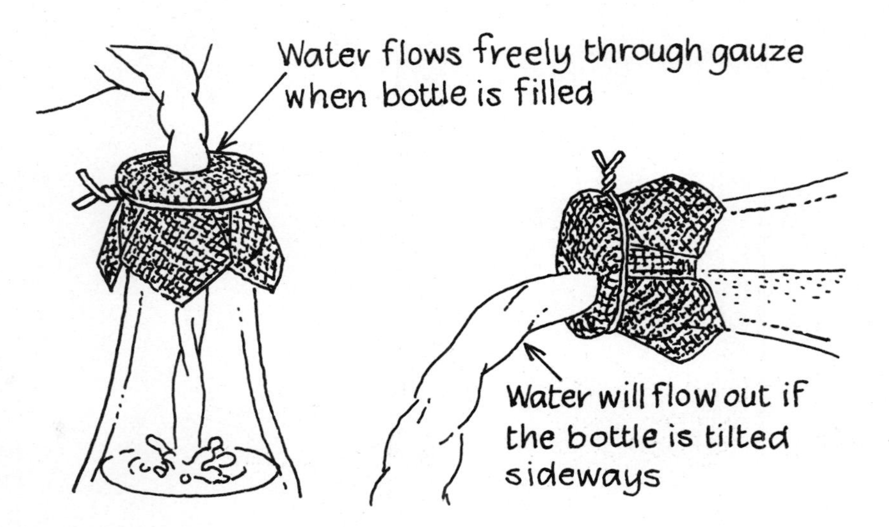

Next, they should half-fill the bottle with water, pouring it through the gauze. If the bottle is tilted sideways, the water will flow out freely. Then ask the children to turn the bottle upside down; the water will not now flow out of the bottle.

If a cocktail stick is inserted through one of the holes in the gauze, it will float to the top of the water, but the water will remain in the bottle.

Scientific notes
A combination of surface tension and air pressure does the trick. Just as in 'Amazing tea strainer', a skin forms over each minute hole and the upward air pressure keeps the water in the bottle.

Science AT1, 10

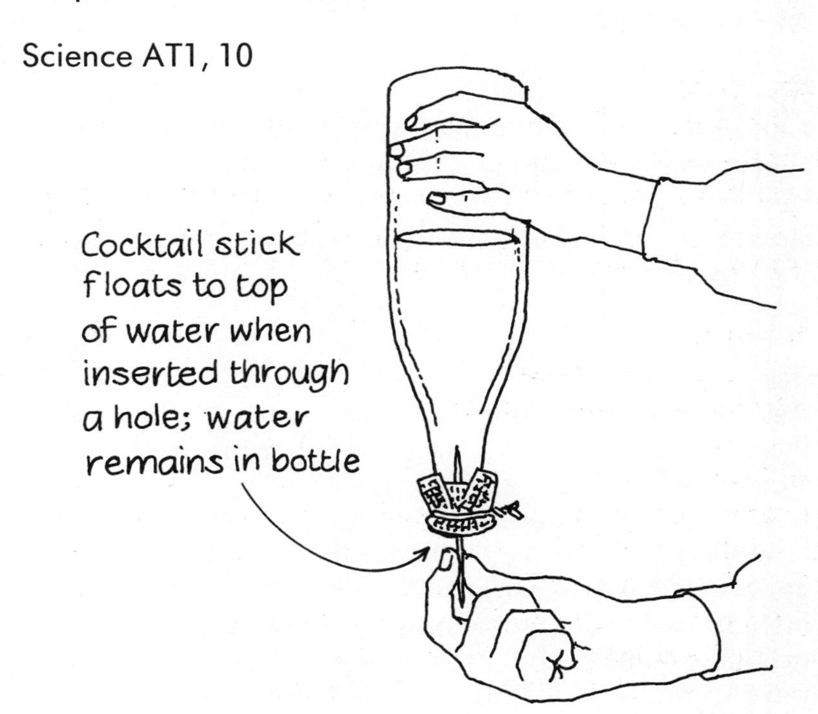

Magic bottle 2

Objective
To show how a light table tennis ball can prevent water from flowing out of a milk bottle.

Age range
Seven to eleven.

Group size
Individuals or pairs.

What you need
Milk bottles, table tennis balls, weighing equipment, thin plastic or paper.

What to do
The children should fill a milk bottle with water so that it is overflowing, and place a table tennis ball on top of the bottle.

Slowly, *using only one hand*, they should turn the bottle upside down. The ball will adhere to the bottle, preventing the water from coming out.

Follow-up
- Ask the children to find the weight of the table tennis ball and the weight of the water in the bottle, and compare the two.
- Ask them to find out what happens if the bottle is only half full. In this case, they will need to hold the ball under the bottle as they turn it.
- Instead of a table tennis ball, the children might try using other items such as a thin piece of plastic or paper. Again, they will have to hold these items on to the bottle as it is turned.

Scientific notes
The air pressure underneath the table tennis ball is sufficient to keep it in the mouth of the bottle, thus preventing the water from escaping.

Science AT1, 10

Inverted glass

Objective
To show how air pressure can prevent water from falling out of a tumbler.

Age range
Nine to eleven.

Group size
Individuals or pairs.

What you need
Tumblers just large enough to fit on the palm of a child's hand, pieces of thin card just large enough to cover the mouth of a tumbler, bowls to catch water.

What to do
First, the children should fill a tumbler with water, making sure it is full to the very top. Then, very carefully, they can place a piece of card on top of the glass. Tell them to press the palm of their hand firmly over the card, and turn the glass upside down over a sink or bowl. When the children take their hand away, the water will stay in the glass with the card still in position, defying the force of gravity.

Card just large enough to cover mouth of tumbler

Tumbler full of water

Follow-up
The older children could try to solve the following problems.
- What is the area of the part of the card that is covering the mouth of the tumbler?
- Given that the air pressure is 1 kilogram per square centimetre (14 pounds per square inch) what pressure in kg is pushing up on this area?

Scientific notes
Air pressure is responsible for the success of this very popular stunt. The air pressure underneath the card is more than strong enough to support the weight of the water in the tumbler.

Science AT1, 10

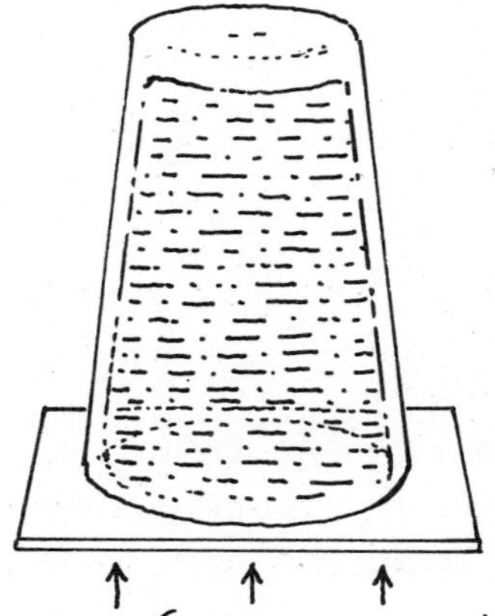

String 'n' things

A piece of string is a most versatile item. As well as tying parcels, playing conkers and making string figures, it can be used for one or two unusual experiments.

Perhaps the most unusual of these is the 'Swinging pendulum'. This item on its own can lead to a great deal of follow-up work.

The 'Pattern-making pendulum' looks simple, but when the strings are either shortened or lengthened, a variety of patterns result.

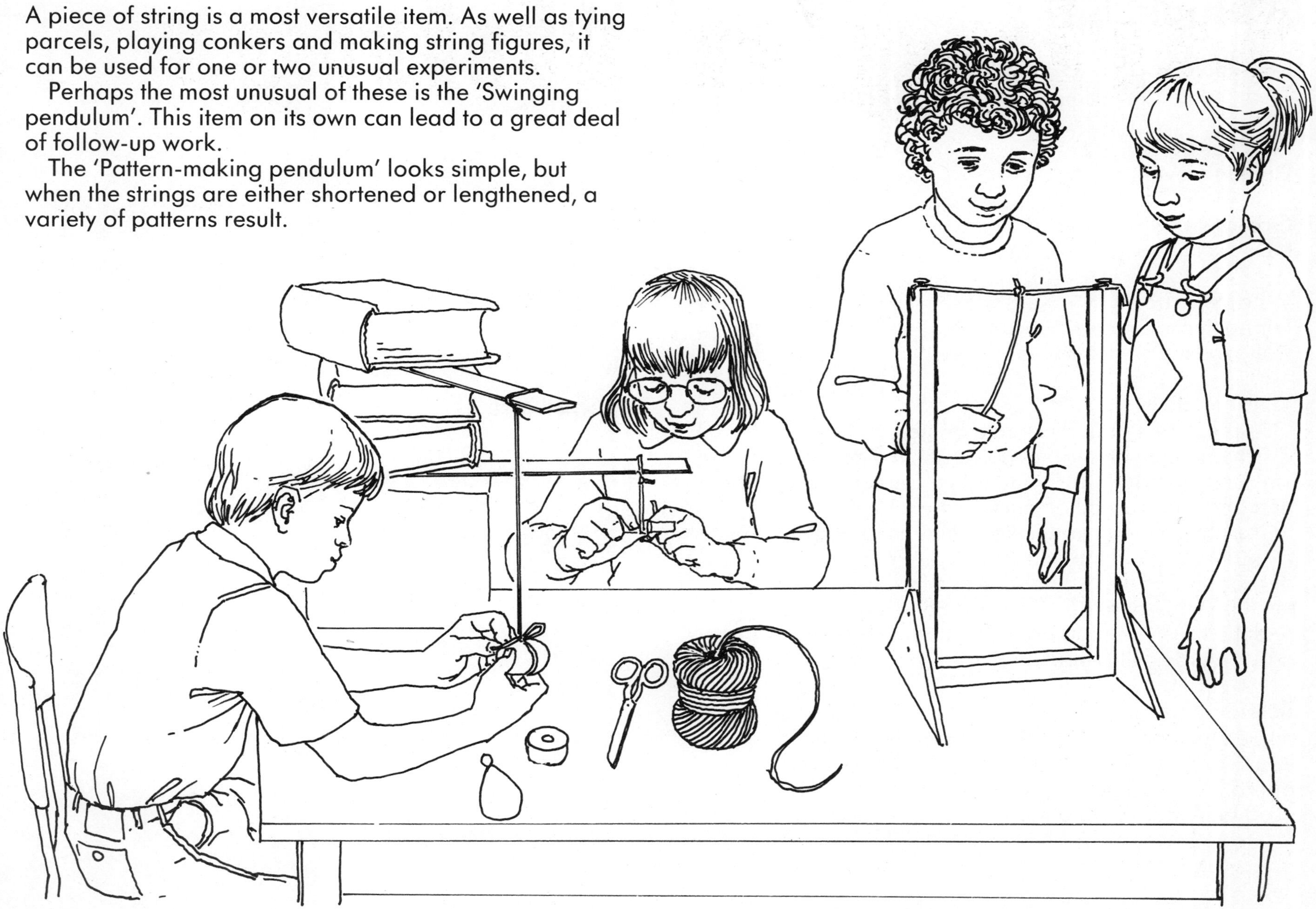

A simple lift

Objective
To demonstrate a simple version of the pulley principle.

Age range
Eight to eleven.

Group size
Pairs.

What you need
For each pair: a cardboard tube, two long pieces of string, a small curtain ring.

What to do
One piece of string (A) should be tied on to the ring, which can then be threaded through the cardboard tube. The second string (B) should be looped through the ring and one end stapled or stuck to the tube as shown.

The children can now take it in turns to perform the experiment. Hold the end of string A in the right hand, and string B in the left hand. Keep the strings taut and the tube will hang. Relax the left hand's grip on string B and the tube will slide down. Pull both ends of the string and the tube will rise.

Scientific notes
Some machines help us to do work, such as lifting a heavy load, by changing the direction of a force operating on the load. Simple pulleys like this are often used to lift heavy weights.

Science AT1, 10

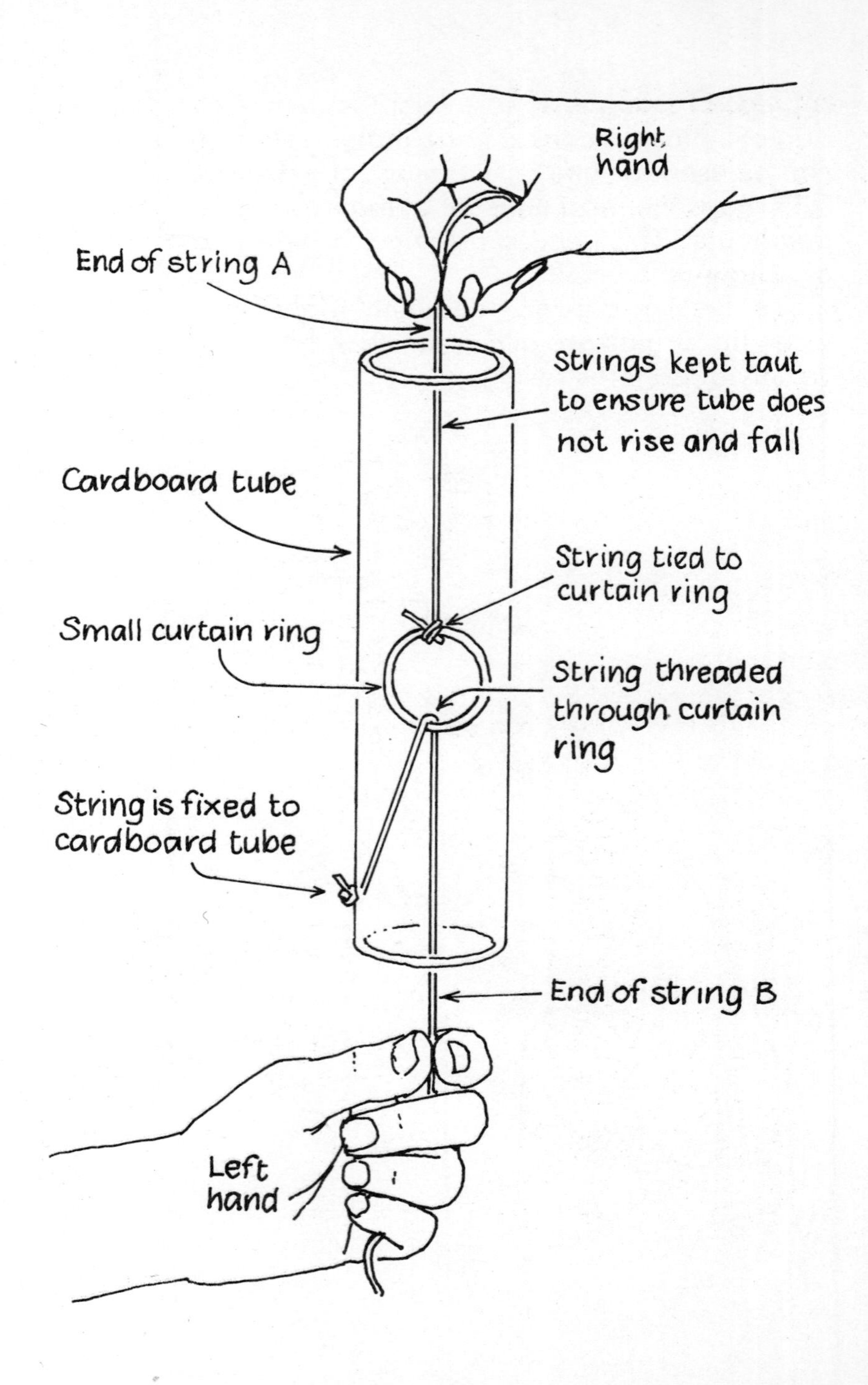

Broom pulley

Objective
To demonstrate a simple pulley system.

Age range
Nine to eleven.

Group size
Large groups.

What you need
For each group: two brooms, a length of rope.

What to do
Ask the children each to hold a broom handle and to stand about a metre apart. Another child should tie one end of the rope to one of the handles and wind the rope around both handles a couple of times as illustrated.

While this child keeps hold of the free end of the rope, the two broom holders should try to keep the handles apart by pulling on them. No matter how hard these children resist, the child holding the rope will be able to bring them together by pulling the rope.

Follow-up
If four children hold the handles, can the rope holder still pull them together? What happens if they increase or decrease the number of times the rope is wrapped around the handles?

Scientific notes
The two brush handles form a combination of pulleys. The more times the rope is wrapped around the handle, the more effective the pull on the rope. This is because the force of the pull is increased by the number of times the rope is wrapped around the handles.

Science AT1, 10

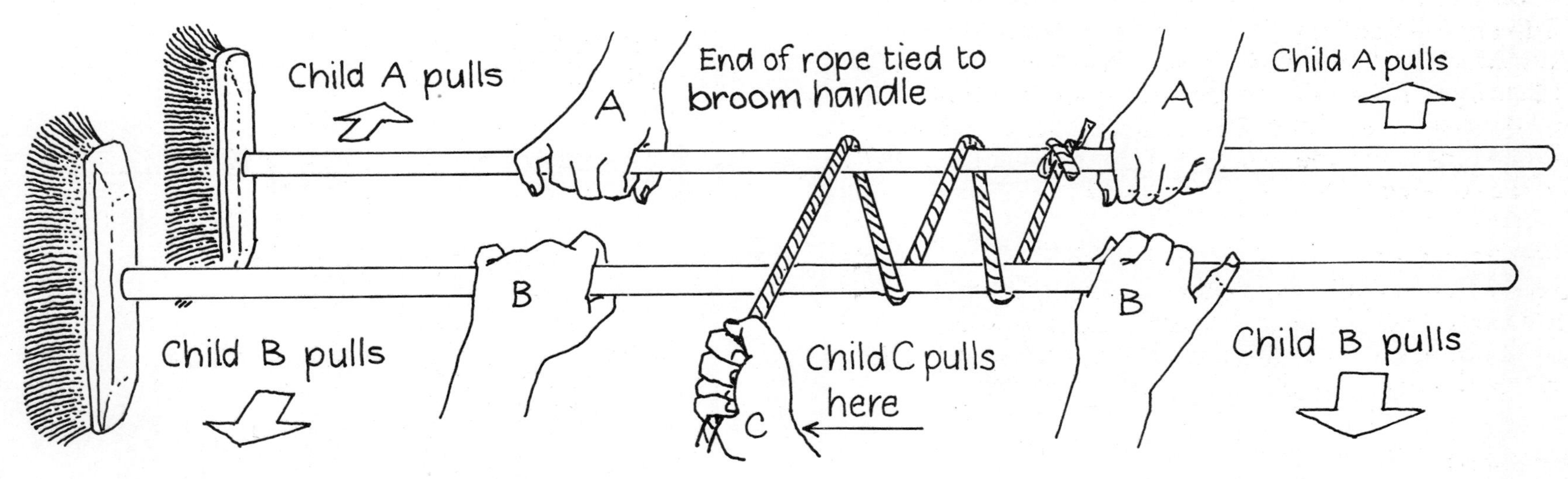

A match for gravity

Objective
To demonstrate that the expected does not always occur.

Age range
Nine to eleven.

Group size
Small groups or the whole class.

What you need
A pencil or piece of square wood of similar size, a piece of string about 1m in length, with a *thin* piece of wood 5cm to 10cm long and slightly thicker than a match tied on at one end, and a heavy bunch of keys at the other.

What to do
When demonstrating this trick, hold the apparatus as shown, at arm's length, with the keys a short distance from the pencil. Ask the children what they think will happen if you release your hold on the thin piece of wood. They will probably predict that the bunch of keys will drop to the floor with a thud.

Let go of the wood – and the result is exactly the opposite of that predicted. The thin piece of wood will wind rapidly and tightly around the pencil, causing the keys to remain suspended in mid air.

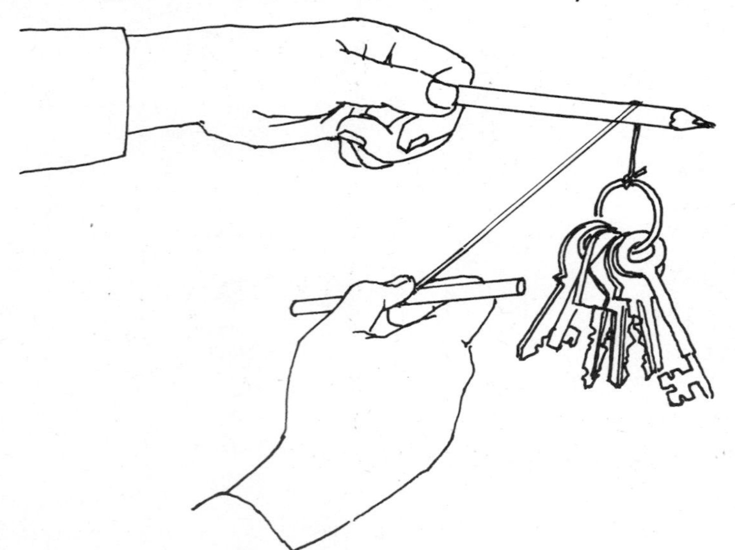

Follow-up
Let the children try the experiment with a different length of string and objects of different weights. Does the weight of the objects make any difference to the number of times the piece of wood winds around the pencil?

Scientific notes
The force exerted on the piece of wood by the falling keys causes the wood to move rapidly up towards the pencil, so that the string wraps around the pencil tightly.

Science AT1, 10

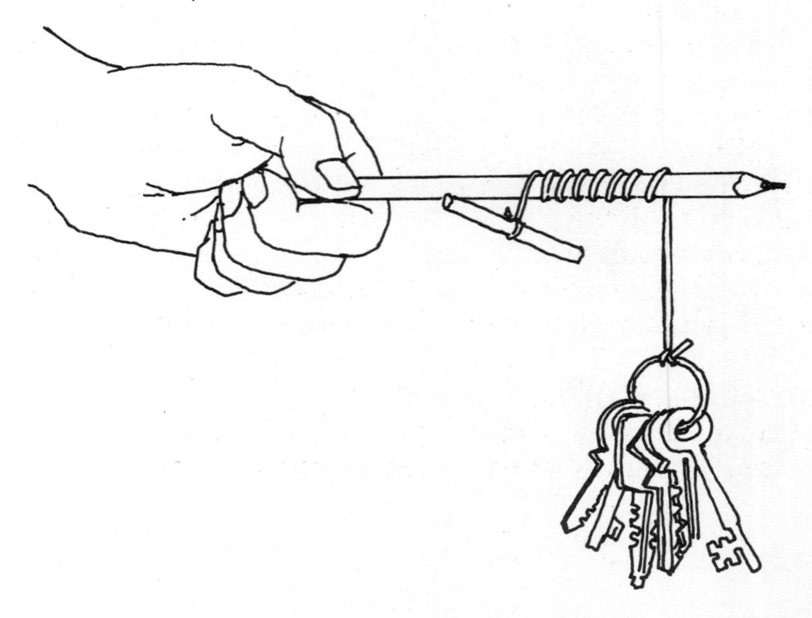

Jumping clown

Objective

To show how a cut-out of a circus clown can be made to move by a series of simple string levers.

Age range

Ten to eleven.

Group size

Individuals or small groups.

What you need

Photocopiable page 119, pieces of thick white card, strong thread, scissors, paper-fasteners, small curtain rings, sticky tape.

What to do

Reproduce the pictures of the clown shown on photocopiable page 119 by tracing or photocopying them on to the white card. Make sure you have two arms and legs for each body! Ask the children to colour the various parts of the clown using felt-tipped pens.

Next, they should cut out the sections, make twelve holes where indicated by black spots, and tie lengths of thread through the holes at the top of each arm and leg. Using brass paper-fasteners they can now assemble the various pieces as illustrated. When they pull the string, the clown's arms and legs will go up and down.

Follow-up

• Can the class design some other characters such as toys and animals that work using a similar system?

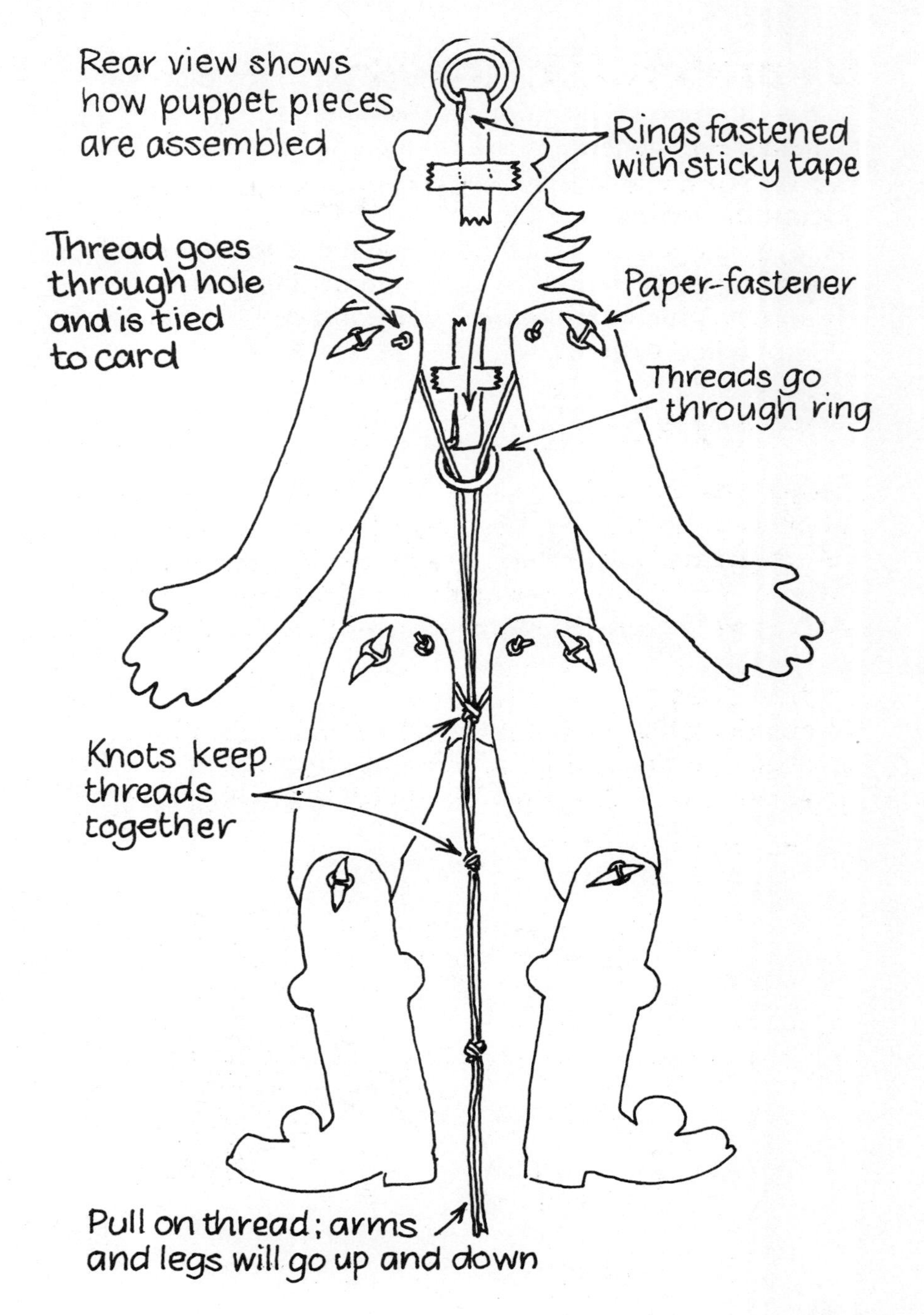

• If the children look in toy shops, they may discover other jumping string puppets. Ask them to find out whether the mechanics are all the same.

Scientific notes

A lever is a simple machine which helps to lift weights. The clown is operated by a system of simple string levers. It is fun to make and work and can lead to more complicated systems.

Science AT1, 10, 13

Swinging pendulums

Objective
To show how the energy from one swinging pendulum can be transferred to a second pendulum, and vice versa.

Age range
Eight to eleven.

Group size
Pairs.

What you need
Two chairs for each pair, string, Plasticine.

What to do
Each pair should tie a two-metre length of string to two chairs, as illustrated.

They should then make two Plasticine balls of equal size and attach each one to a piece of string about 50cm in length.

These strings should then be tied to the horizontal string between the two chairs. If a loop is made at the end of each of the two strings, it will be easier to move them along the horizontal string at a later stage in the experiment.

If the children now start one of the pendulums swinging, after a few seconds the other pendulum will start to swing as well. As this happens, the first one will slow down and stop. This swinging and stopping will alternate until eventually both Plasticine balls slow down and stop.

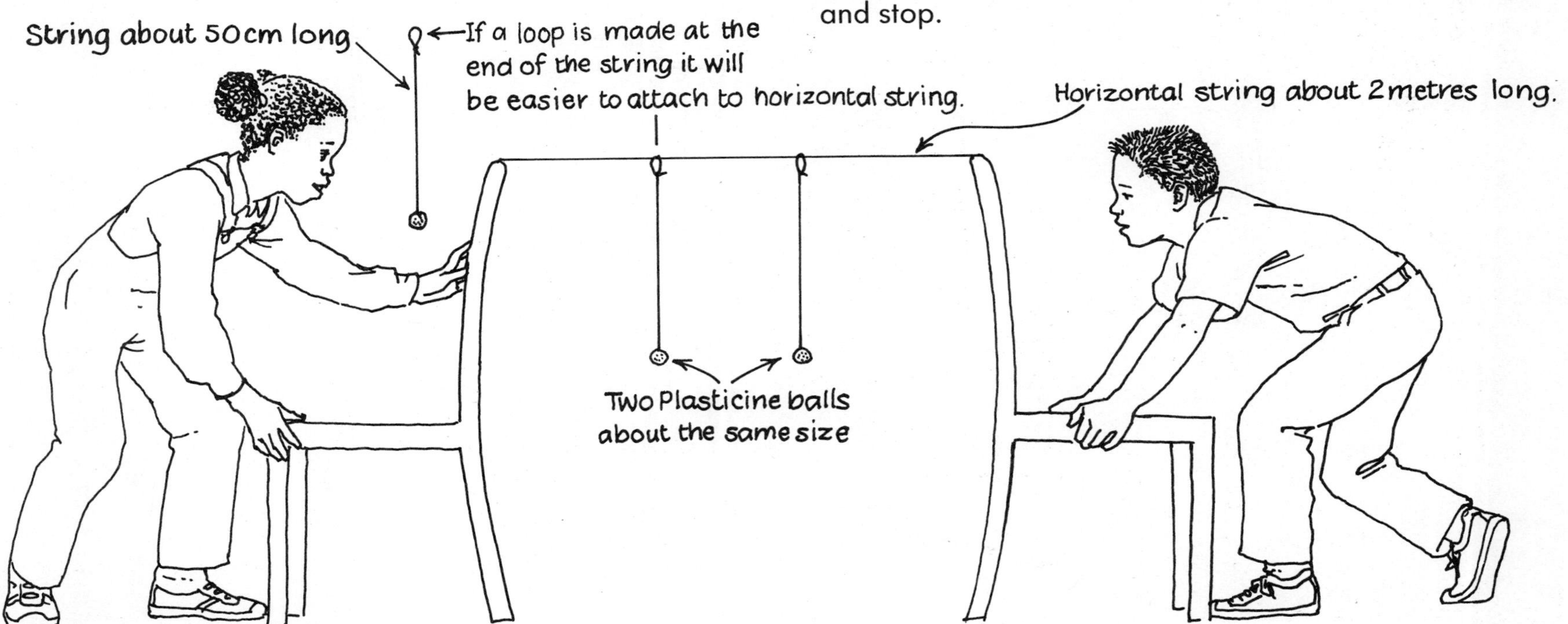

Follow-up

Ask the children the following questions.

- Does it make any difference whether the horizontal string is slack or taut?
- What happens if the pendulums are moved further apart?
- Does it make any difference if the weight of one of the pendulums is reduced?
- What happens if one string is shorter than the other?
- What happens if there are three pendulums?
- What variations can be introduced? (For example, the children could introduce a third chair and a second horizontal string as shown.)

Scientific notes

Each swing of a pendulum gives the horizontal string between the chairs a twist. This transfers energy to the other pendulum, which then starts swinging. Thus the second pendulum takes energy from the first pendulum until the first pendulum has lost all its energy. This transference of energy then begins to take place in the opposite direction until, eventually, they both slow down and stop completely.

Science AT1, 13

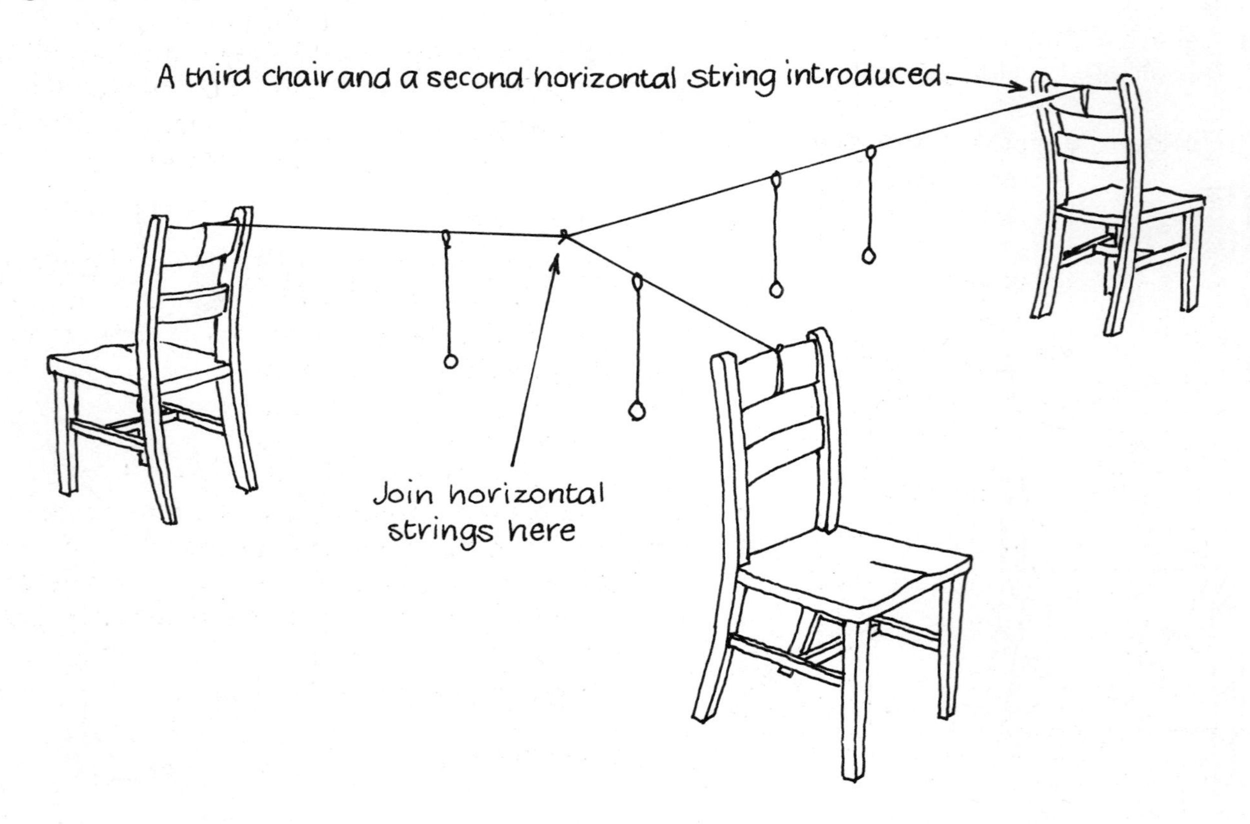

Pattern-making pendulum

Objective
To demonstrate how swinging pendulums of different lengths can create a variety of patterns.

Age range
Eight to eleven.

Group size
Pairs or small groups.

What you need
Paper cups, two long pieces of string the same length for each group, dark coloured sugar paper, salt.

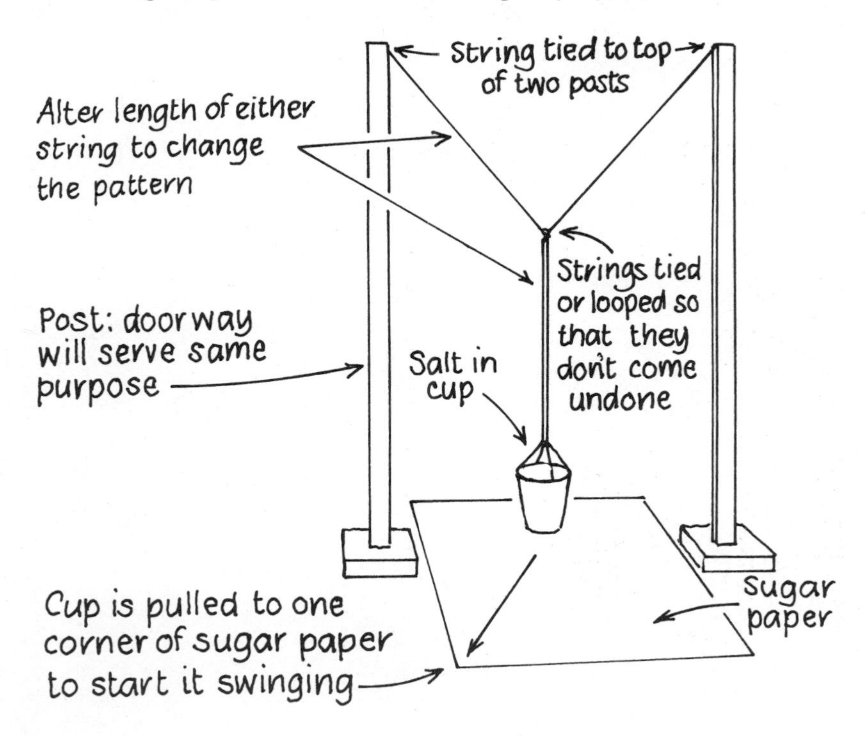

What to do
The children should first tie the ends of the two pieces of string to the tops of two upright posts (a doorway will do if nothing else is suitable). Next they should loop or tie the two strings together about halfway down, allowing the remaining ends to hang freely. It should resemble a letter 'Y'.

Meanwhile, one child can make one small hole in the bottom of a paper cup, and two more on opposite sides of the rim. The two hanging pieces of string can then be tied to the top of the cup. Ask the children to make sure it is not lop-sided. They can now fill the cup with salt (covering the hole in the bottom of the cup while they do so) and place the sugar paper beneath it.

Still covering the hole, they should pull the cup to one corner of the sugar paper and as they let go, start it swinging. As the cup goes to and fro, the falling salt will form some interesting patterns on the sugar paper.

Follow-up
Ask the children to see what type of pattern is formed if they alter the length of the strings, or if they try swinging the cup in different directions – back and forth or sideways, for example.

Scientific notes
The string and cup act like two different pendulums. One is swinging back and forth between the posts, the other to and fro across the sugar paper. This combined action causes the cup to swing in a regular manner and the falling salt creates some interesting patterns.

If you alter the length of either the upper or the lower string, the pattern will change.

Science AT1, 13

The optical pendulum

Objective
To show how a pendulum that swings in a straight line appears to move in a circle.

Age range
Seven to eleven.

Group size
Small groups.

What you need
For each group, a pendulum made by fixing a weight to the end of a length of string, a pair of dark sunglasses.

What to do
Ask one child in each group to hold the pendulum, or fasten it to an overhead fixture. The children should make the pendulum swing in a straight line from left to right. Now ask them, one at a time, to look at the swinging pendulum while holding one lens of the sunglasses to their right eye. Their left eye should be clear, and they should keep both eyes open while looking at the swinging pendulum. Amazingly, the pendulum will now appear to be swinging in a circle.

Next, ask the children to look at the pendulum with one lens of the sunglasses over the other eye, again keeping both eyes open. The pendulum will now appear to be moving in a circle in the opposite direction.

Follow-up
Ask the children to consider the following questions.
- Does the length of the string make any difference?
- What happens if the experiment is done against a

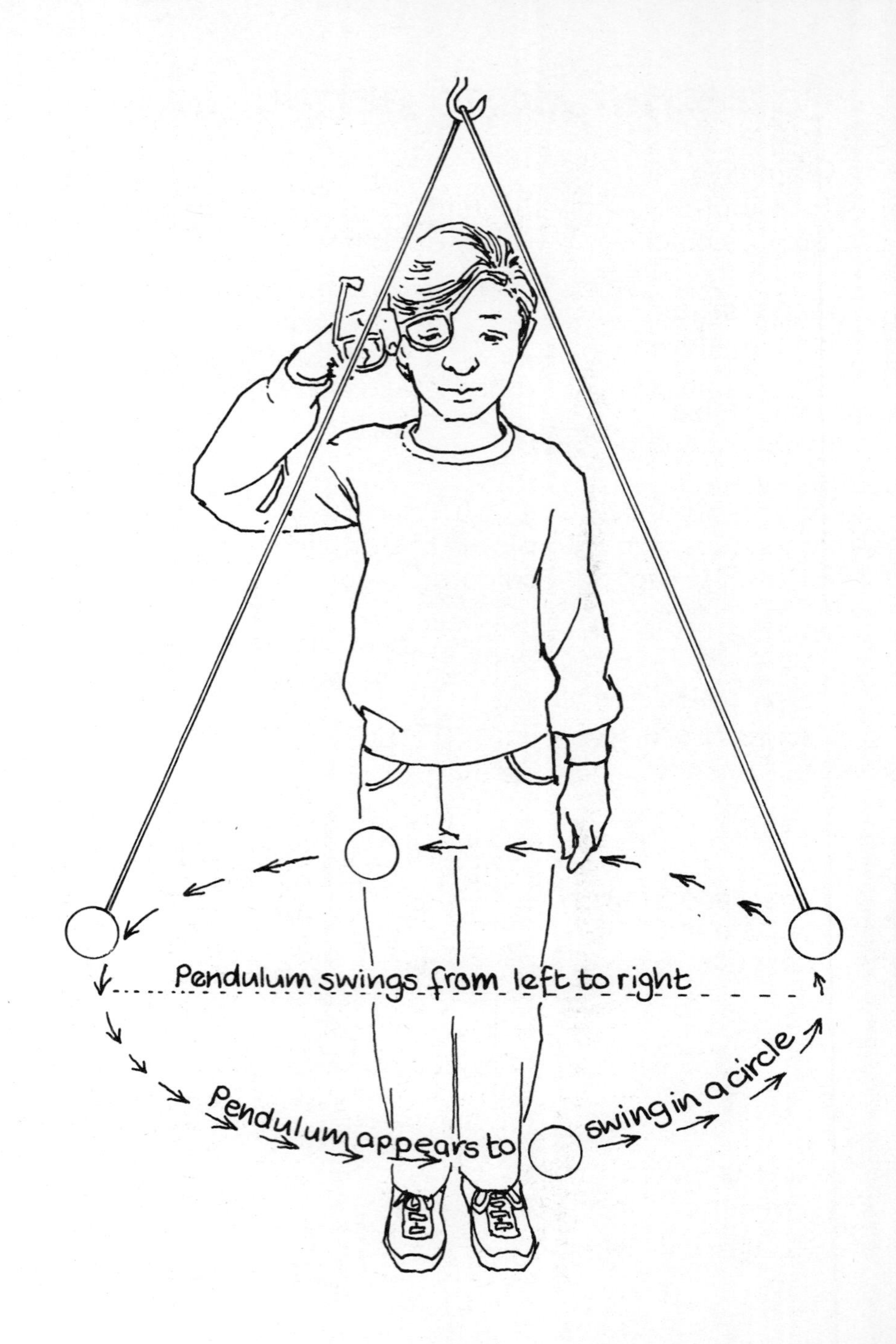

dark background? What if it is done against a light background?
• Would a background wallpaper with vertical, horizontal or other designs make any difference to the effects seen?
• Is there a difference if the experiment is done in bright sunlight as opposed to electric light?
• What effects are seen if the swinging pendulum is observed through different coloured cellophane?

Scientific notes

This illusion is thought to arise from the fact that darkened retinal images are more slowly transmitted to the brain than bright images. The optical illusion is created when the brain combines the two images.

Note that not everyone will be able to observe the circular motion of the pendulum.

Science AT1, 3, 10

Balance

Have you ever wondered how Blondin was able to walk across the Niagara Falls on a tightrope? Have you ever sat in a circus tent and held your breath as a tightrope walker walked across in mid-air? They used a pole which helped them to keep their balance. They had to know all about the centre of gravity and how they could alter it in order not to fall.

There are many amazing balances in this section to try without having to brave the high wire. Most of the items used can probably be found in the kitchen or garage.

Some of the balances will look impossible, and even when you succeed, you may still wonder how they work.

The centre of gravity

Objective
To demonstrate what 'the centre of gravity' means.

Age range
Eight to eleven.

Group size
The whole class.

What you need
A ruler, stick-on letters to spell the word 'gravity'.

What to do
Stick the letters on the ruler, spacing them out. Ensure that the letter 'V' is in the exact centre of the ruler.

Ask the children, 'What do we mean by the centre of gravity?' A whole variety of replies will come forth. Tell them that the centre of 'gravity' is the letter 'V'. After the groans have died down show them the ruler, pointing out that the letter 'V' is in the exact centre.

Put your forefinger under the letter 'V' and the ruler will balance on it. 'The centre of gravity,' you explain, 'is the exact point at which an object will balance.'

I have found that this fun approach to the question acts as a visual aid to understanding the principle.

Follow-up
Balance the ruler on your index fingers, one supporting each end as in the illustration, and ask one of the childen to put a heavy object on one end. Ask the class to guess where the centre of gravity might be now.

To find it, slowly try to move your hands together. At first, the hand at the end of the ruler where the weight is will not move. The reason for this is increased friction because of the weight on the ruler, which stops the finger from moving. There is less friction at the other end, so that finger will move more easily. Eventually, as the moving finger draws closer to the weighted end, the other finger will also move. The point at which the fingers meet will be the centre of gravity.

Scientific notes

The centre of gravity is the point at which an object will balance. When there is no weight on the ruler, the balance point will be the exact centre. The heavier the object placed on the end of the ruler, the nearer to that end of the ruler the centre of gravity will be.

Science AT1, 10, 13

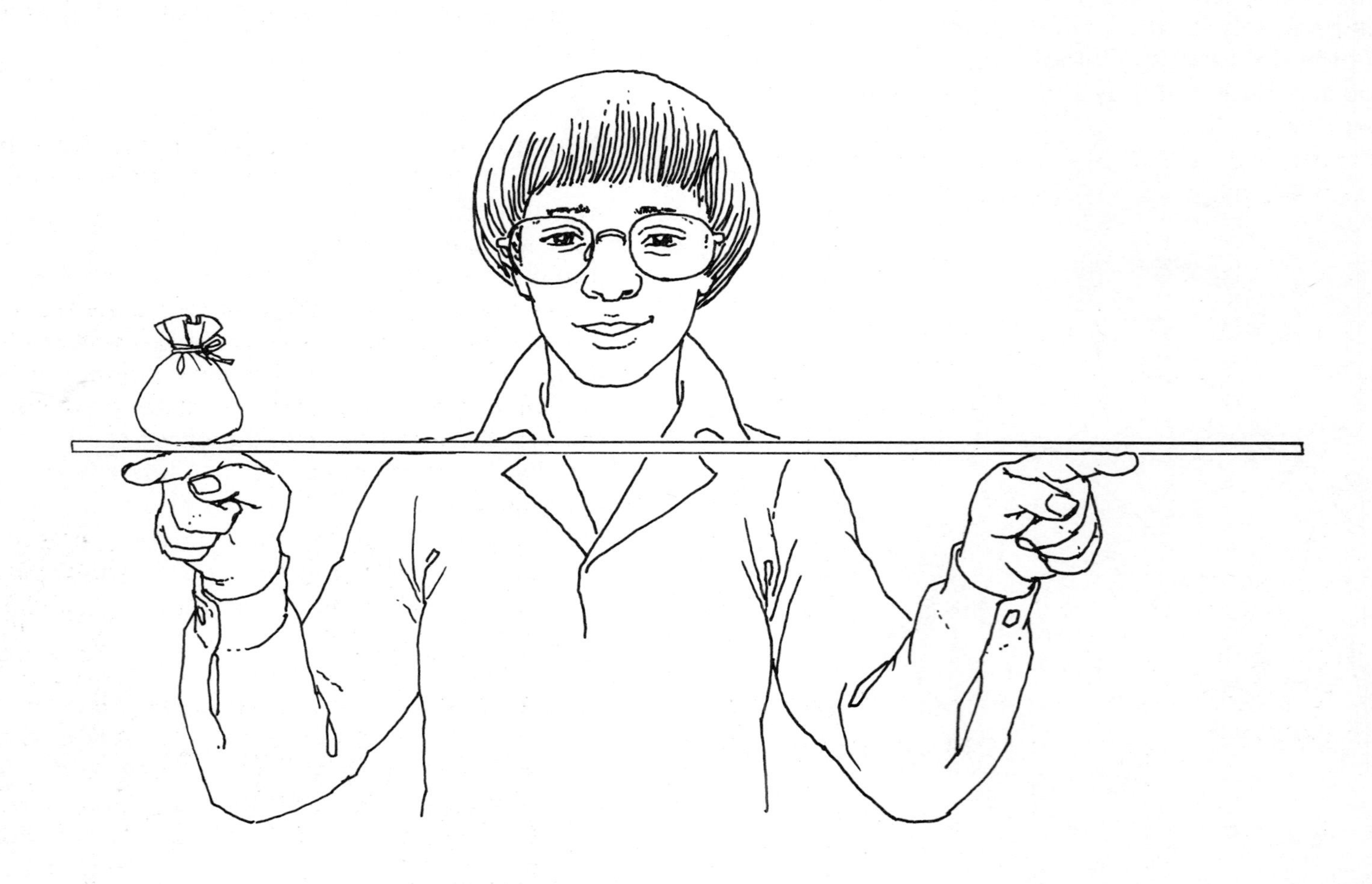

Balancing ladles

Objective
To find the centre of gravity when balancing utensils.

Age range
Nine to eleven.

Group size
Pairs.

What you need
For each pair: a plastic drinks bottle, two ladles with hooks, a plastic plate, Blu-Tack, a few coins.

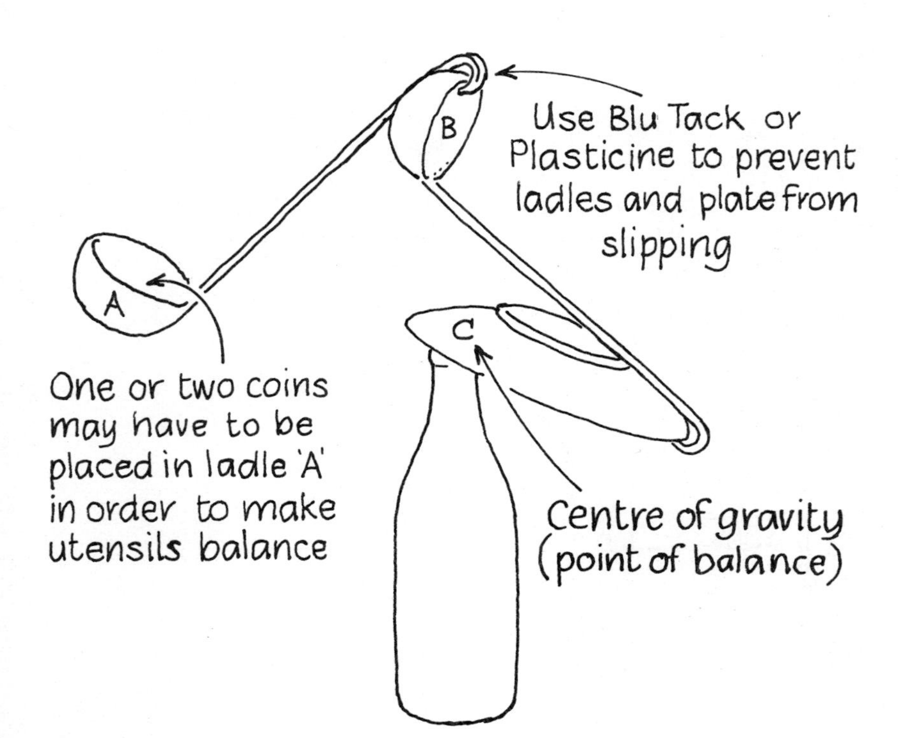

What to do
Working with a partner, each child should try to balance the utensils as shown in the illustration. It is a good idea if one of the children holds the bottle steady, while the other concentrates on the ladles and plate.

It is essential that the ends of the ladles grip very tightly. To ensure this the children should place a piece of Blu-Tack between the ends. One or two coins may have to be placed in ladle A in order to make the utensils balance.

Follow-up
Ask the children to locate and explain the centre of gravity. See if they can create a balance of their own using other utensils.

Scientific notes
The centre of gravity of an object is the point through which the whole weight of the object seems to exert its force. When we want to balance anything we look for the point of balance. The utensils behave as one unit, and the point of balance is at point C.

Science AT1, 10, 13

The chair challenge

Objective
To show how the centre of gravity can prevent someone from getting up from a chair.

Age range
Five to eleven.

Group size
Pairs or larger groups.

What you need
A dining chair for each group; make sure the children can reach the floor when sitting back.

What to do
One of the children should sit in the chair. Her feet must touch the floor and be kept together, and her back must remain upright against the back of the chair. Challenge her to stand up while keeping that position, without using her hands. She will find it impossible.

Scientific notes
When you are seated in a chair the centre of gravity is at the base of your spine. By trying to stand up with your back straight, you prevent the centre of gravity from moving to a position above your feet. Only by leaning forward can your muscles exert sufficient force to enable you to stand up.

Science AT1, 10, 13

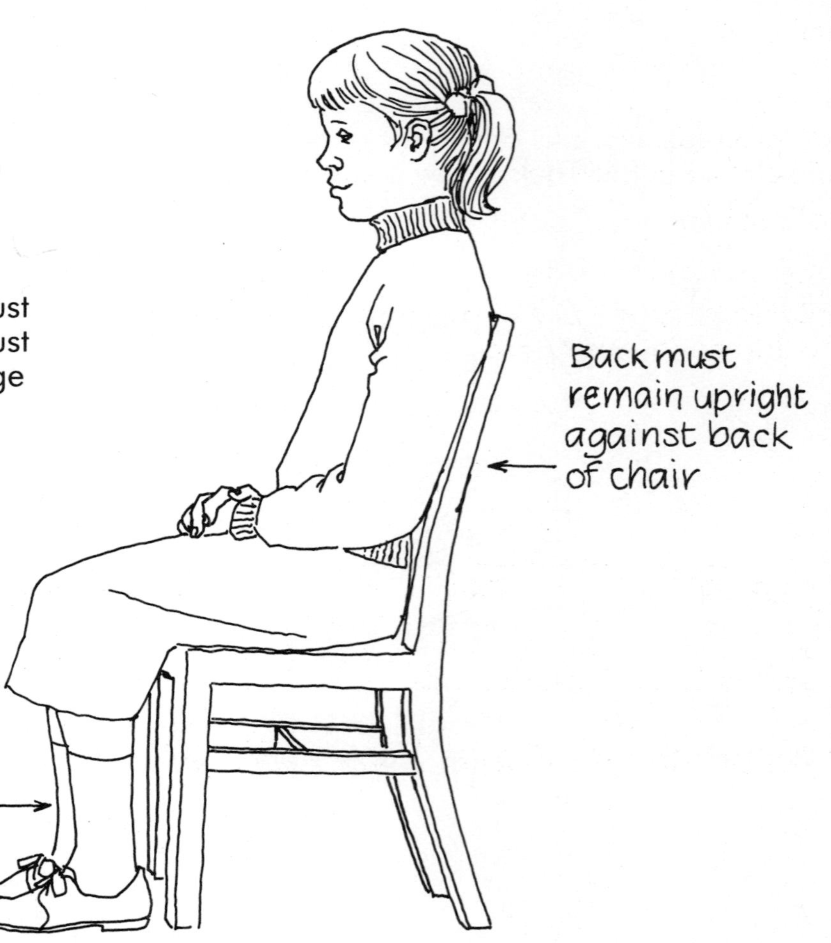

Peg and belt

Objective
To find the centre of gravity when balancing a wooden peg and a leather belt.

Age range
Nine to eleven.

Group size
Individuals or pairs.

What you need
Lengths of wood about 7cm by 2cm, a junior hacksaw, heavy leather belts.

What to do
Ask the children to cut the pieces of wood with the junior hacksaw to the shape illustrated.

The children should then place the belt in the slot as shown. Next, show them how to put the end of the peg on a fingertip, so that it balances. The belt may have to be adjusted until the exact balance point is found. (A good idea is to mark one belt at this point during a practice run, to facilitate your demonstration.)

Scientific notes
In order for the peg to balance on the fingertip, the centre of gravity must be at the point where the peg rests on the finger. The position of the centre of gravity can be altered by adjusting the belt.

Science AT1, 10, 13

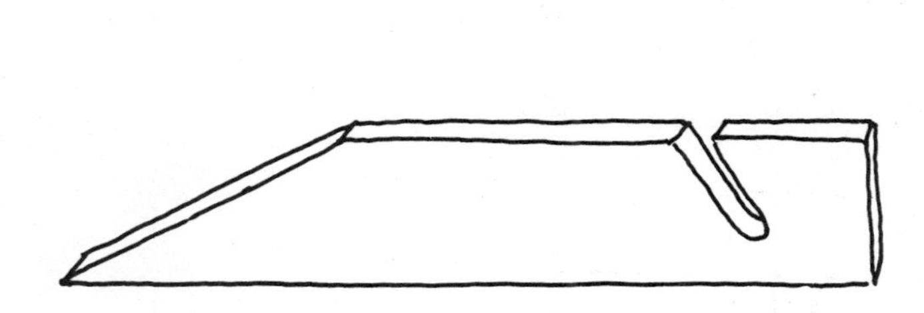
Wooden peg about 7cm × 2cm

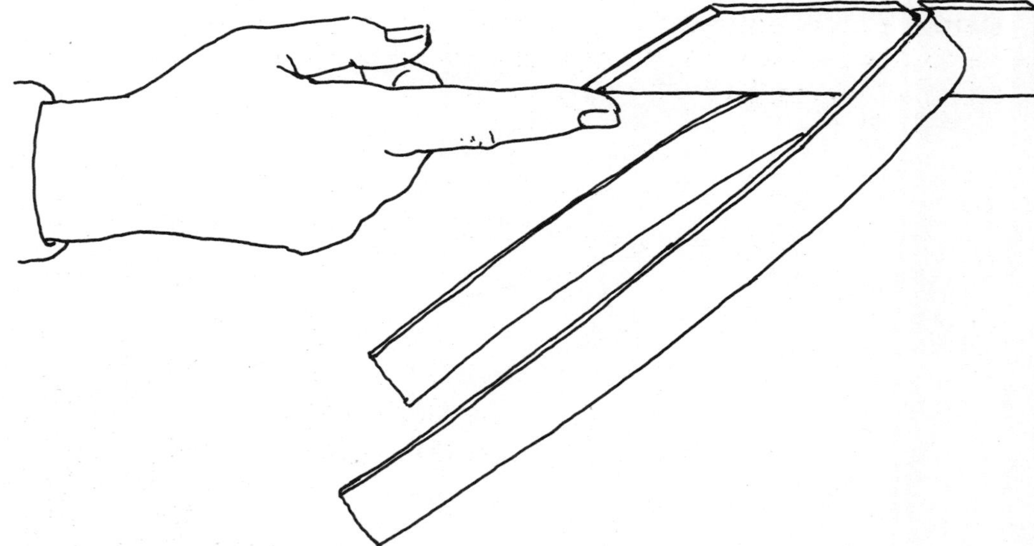

Dangling hammer

Objective
To find the centre of gravity when balancing a hammer and a wooden ruler.

Age range
Eight to eleven.

Group size
Pairs or small groups.

What you need
Hammers, wooden rulers or pieces of wood of similar size (do not use plastic rulers), elastic bands.

What to do
Ask the children to place the elastic band round the ruler, wrapping it round a couple of times if it is too slack.

Next they should put the hammer under the elastic band so that it hangs down from the ruler at an angle.

If the end of the ruler is now placed on the edge of a table, with a little bit of adjustment the hammer and ruler will balance in a way that initially seems to defy gravity. The illustration will make it clear.

Follow-up
Instead of using the table, let the children place a finger under the ruler and balance it on that instead.

Scientific notes
It is the weight of the hammer head that helps to create the illusion that this balance is impossible. The centre of gravity or point of balance is at the point where the ruler rests on the table edge or fingertip.

Science AT1, 10, 13

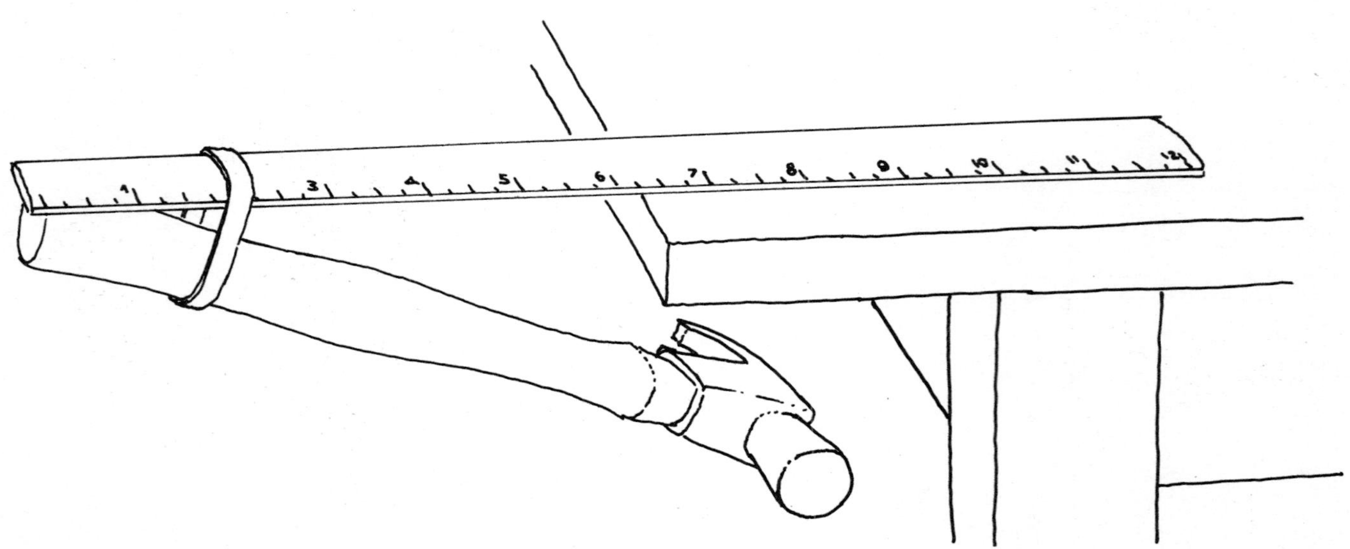

Balancing forks

Objective
To find the centre of gravity when balancing two forks and a coin.

Age range
Eight to eleven.

Group size
Individuals.

What you need
For each child: two four-pronged forks, a two pence coin (test to make sure this fits snugly between the prongs; if the gap is too wide, use a thicker coin).

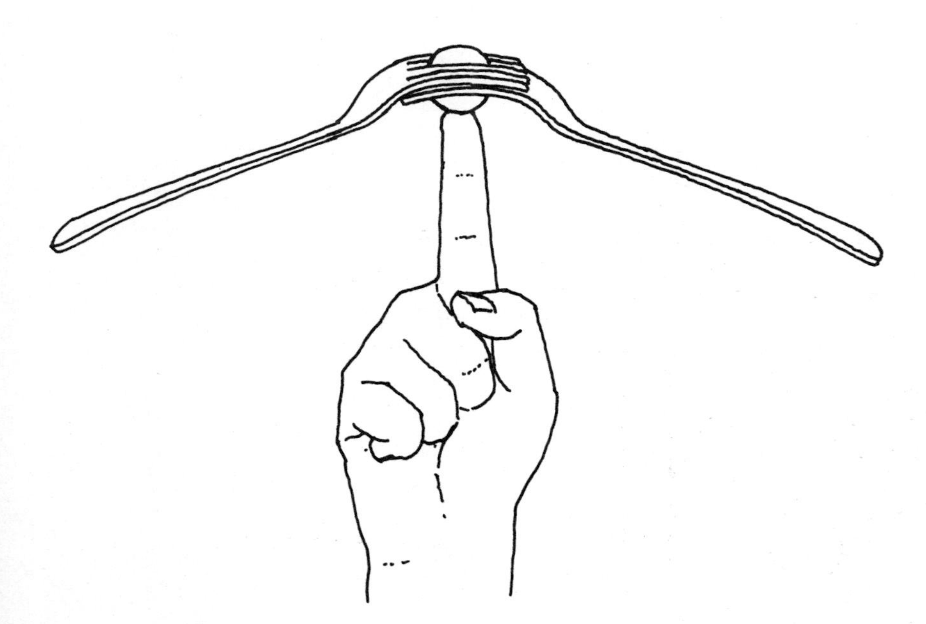

What to do
The two forks should be placed together so that the prongs overlap, as illustrated. Ask the children to place the coin between the middle two prongs of the forks, and to put a fingertip under the edge of the coin. If this is done successfully, the forks will balance in an amazing way. (If only three-pronged forks or ones with heavy handles are available, there may be some difficulty achieving the balance.)

This balance looks impossible because the entire weight of both forks is on the outer edge of the coin.

Follow-up
The children could try balancing the coin and forks on the edge of a glass or the end of a pencil.

Scientific notes
The handles of the forks curve in towards your finger. This moves the centre of gravity or point of balance to the spot where the coins rests on your finger.

Science AT1, 10, 13

Mugged

Objective
To show how four knives, when carefully balanced, can support a heavy weight.

Age range
Nine to eleven.

Group size
Pairs.

What you need
For each pair: five coffee mugs (four of which should be of equal height), four table knives.

What to do
Ask the children to place the four same-size mugs in a square formation 15 to 20cm apart, and very carefully to balance the four knives on top, as illustrated, until they have made a sort of bridge. They may need a little practice at first to do this.

Next, ask them to take the fifth coffee mug and place it on top of the knives. The knives will support it.

Follow-up
- Let the children experiment to discover how heavy an object the 'bridge of knives' will support.
- Can they devise a similar set-up using five, six, seven or more knives?
- Could they use other items instead of knives – for example, knitting needles or straws?

Scientific notes
Each knife is supported at both ends, so they each share the burden when the extra weight is added.

Science AT1, 10, 13

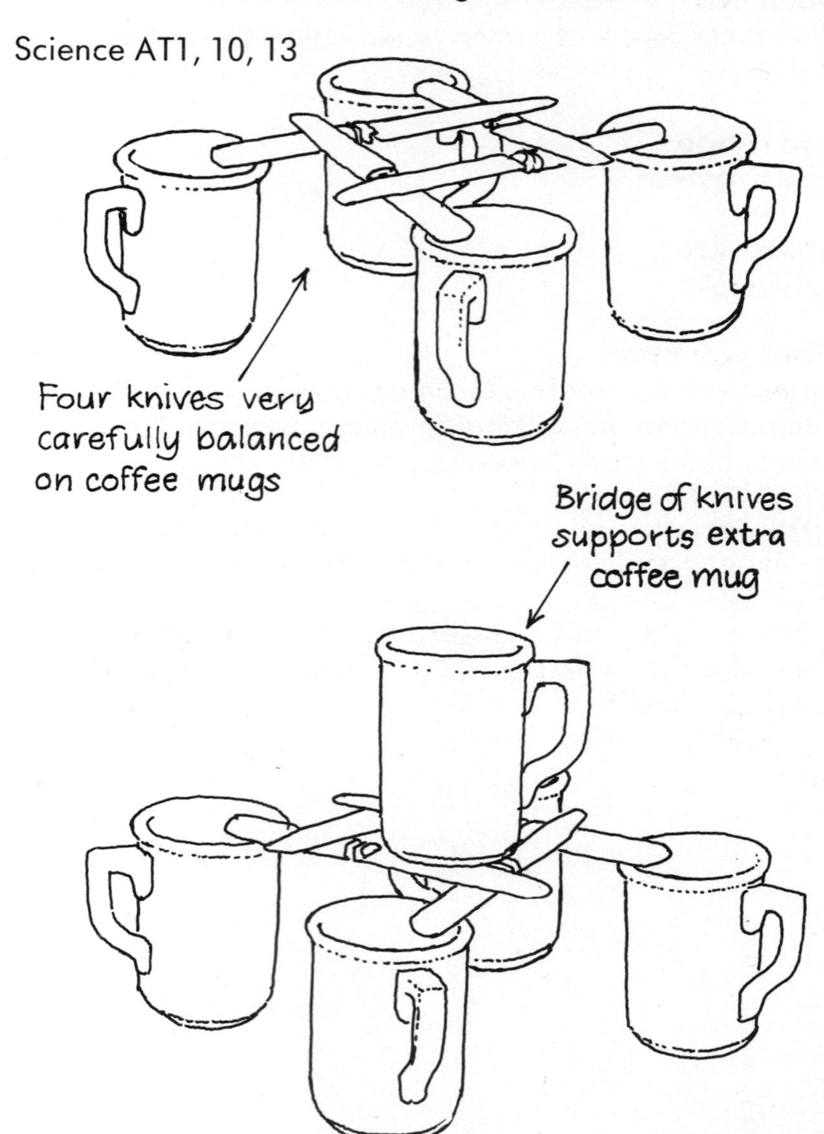

Balancing a broom

Objective
To balance a broom and a chair, demonstrating the position of the centre of gravity.

Age range
Nine to eleven.

Group size
Large groups.

What you need
For each group: three open-backed chairs, a broom, a piece of wood about a metre long.

What to do
Ask the children to place two of the chairs back to back, just under a metre apart, and to place the piece of wood across their backs.

They should then lay the broom handle across the piece of wood and hang the third chair on the end of the handle as illustrated.

Everything will balance, despite the heavy weight of the chair, although the children may need to adjust the hanging chair and the broom handle until they find the exact point of blance.

Scientific notes
The chair and broom balance because the centre of gravity of the hanging chair is exactly at the point of support on the piece of wood.

Science AT1, 10, 13

Balancing bottle and umbrella

Objective
To show how a bottle and an umbrella can seem to defy the laws of gravity.

Age range
Ten to eleven.

Group size
Small groups.

What you need
For each group: a thick plastic bottle, a piece of rope about two metres in length, an umbrella (child or adult size) with a curved handle which must fit loosely into the neck of the bottle.

What to do
Demonstrate the first balance, putting the handle of the umbrella into the bottle and balancing the bottle on your forefinger. You may have to adjust the bottle until you find the exact balance point. Then get the children to copy this.

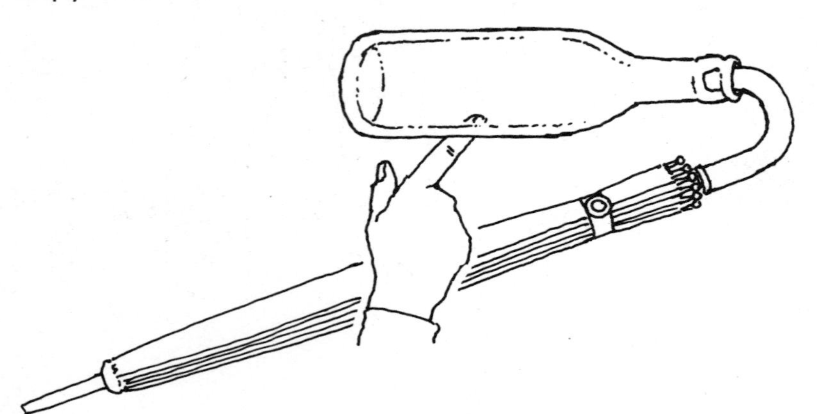

Next, two children should hold the rope between them, keeping it steady and taut. Another child can balance the bottle and the umbrella on the rope as illustrated. The bottle position may have to be adjusted as before, to locate the centre of gravity.

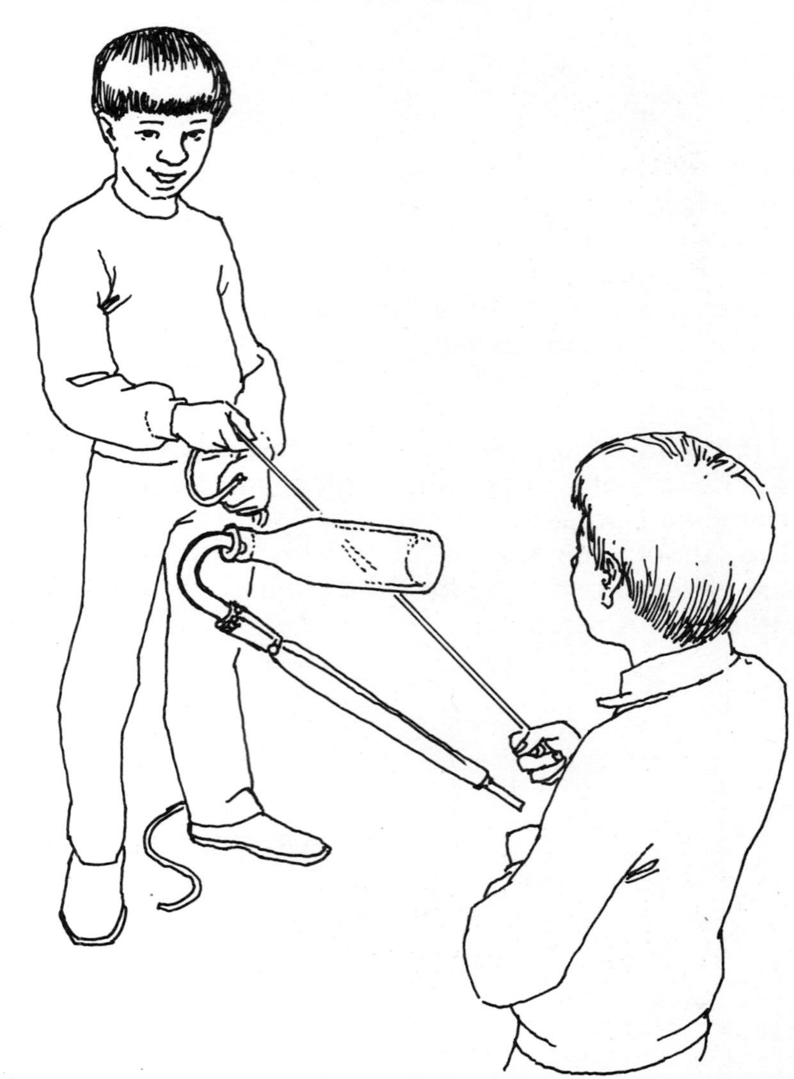

Follow-up

Ask the children to open the umbrella, put the handle in the neck of the bottle and balance the bottle on the rope as in the previous experiment, to find out whether the balance point will change now the umbrella is opened.

Scientific notes

In the first balance the centre of gravity (or balance point) is at the point where the bottle rests on the finger.

In the rope balances, the centre of gravity is at the point where the bottle rests on the rope.

Science AT1, 10, 13

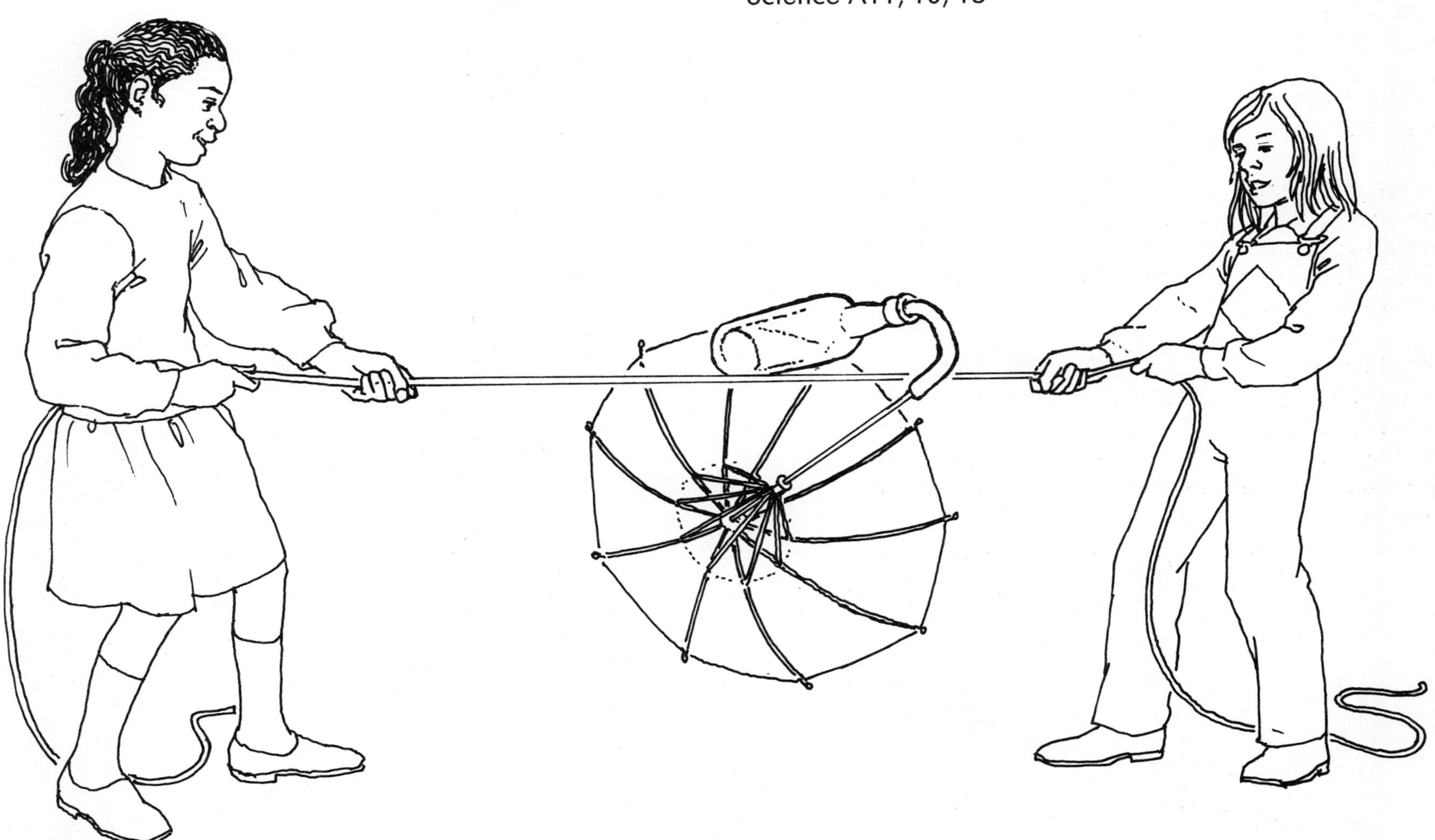

Brain teasers

One area that still retains a great deal of mystery is that of the mind and its capabilities. People are always intrigued by tricks that are mentally baffling.

Most of the activities in this section would link well with work in mathematics. Some of the activities rely on mental dexterity and will leave the onlookers puzzled, with no visible explanation. Some of the others, such as 'Upside down words' and 'Colour words', will inspire children to try them out on their friends, but all the activities will give food for thought.

Carrot

Objective
To test a prediction.

Age range
Eight to eleven.

Group size
Large groups or the whole class.

What you need
A card with the word 'CARROT' printed on it.

What to do
Place the CARROT card face down on the table so that no one can read it. Tell the children that you are going to ask them to answer some simple sums, and they are to answer them all together.

2 + 2 =
4 + 4 =
8 + 8 =
16 + 16 =

The first time they do it is as a practice. Tell them you are going to go through the sums three more times, fairly quickly, and then you are going to ask them to name something. They are to answer immediately and with the first thing they think of.

Repeat the 'test' three times. At the end of this, say quickly: 'Name a vegetable'. You may be surprised to find that a lot of the children say 'carrot'. Turn over the card to show them your prediction.

Follow-up
The children can try this individually in the playground and at home, and tabulate their results.

Scientific notes
Some people say that when we add up quickly a red or orange flash goes through our brain and that this prompts the association with carrots. It is certainly true that a lot of people automatically say 'carrot' when asked the question. Whether this explanation accounts for it is not clear; however, it definitely works more times than not.

Maths AT3

Colour words

Objective
To show how difficult it is to do two things at the same time.

Age range
Eight to eleven.

Group size
Large groups or the whole class.

What you need
Three sets of words on cards labelled A, B and C, written in different colours as shown.

Card A

BOOK	written in green
PLAY	written in blue
FILM	written in red

Card B

RED	written in green
GREEN	written in blue
BLUE	written in red

Card C

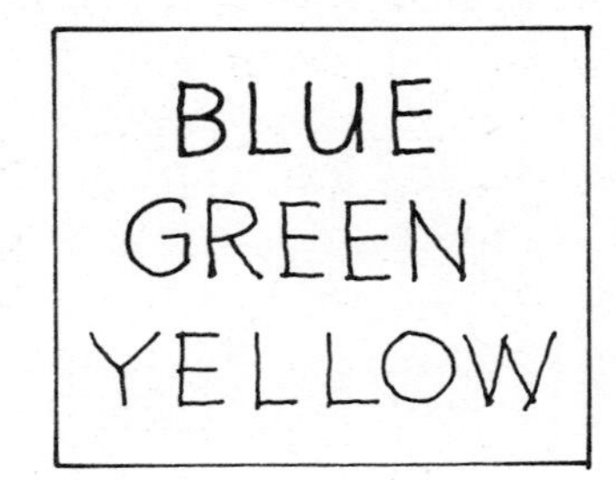

written in orange

written in black

written in blue

What to do
Hold card A in your hand, with the words facing you. Tell the children that there are some words on the card, written in different colours. They are to ignore the colours and just read the words, fairly quickly and all together.

Turn over the card and tell them to read the words. They will probably read them correctly.

Next take card B, keeping the words facing you. Explain to the children that again there are three words written in different colours. This time they are to *ignore the words* and say what colours the words are written in.

Turn over the card and ask them to say the colours. There will probably be confusion. Some will read the words instead of saying what colours the words are written in.

Try the same thing again, this time with card C.

Follow-up

Get the children to make a series of lists of words written in a variety of colours and try this experiment on each other and on friends.

Scientific notes

It is difficult at first to say the colours and ignore the words, because when confronted with a word there is always a temptation to read it. It is particularly difficult when the written word is also the name of a colour.

The longer the list and the quicker you try it, the harder it is to do.

Science AT1, 3

Can you count?

Objective
To see whether, using their eyes only, the children can count the number of times a certain letter appears in a piece of writing.

Age range
Nine to eleven.

Group size
Individuals, groups or the whole class.

What you need
The following words written on a piece of card: 'On Friday, Fred finally received the result of fifteen years of frustrating scientific research. His future was now assured. He went off to celebrate with his friends, Frank and Fiona.'

What to do
One at a time, using only their eyes, the group should count the number of 'F's there are in the above piece of writing.

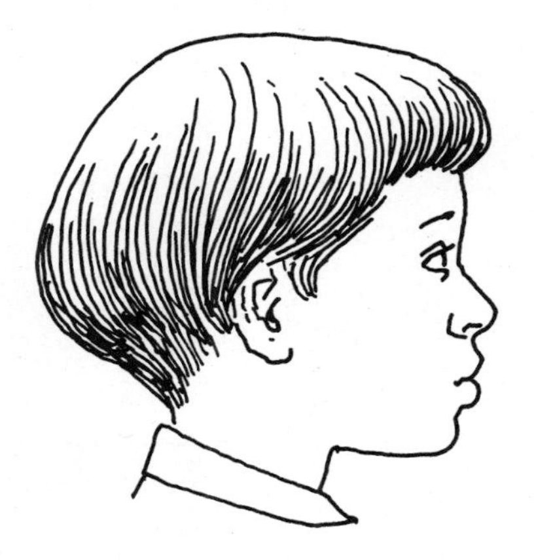

Follow-up
- Ask the class to make up a similar piece of writing, using a different repeated letter.
- Ask them to read the following:

WHEN YOU CAREFULLY READ THE
THE WORDS IN A PARAGRAPH LIKE
LIKE THIS ONE IT IS EASY TO
TO MAKE A MISTAKE. IN
IN FACT YOU MIGHT BE
BE MAKING ONE RIGHT NOW
NOW UNLESS YOU ARE
ARE READING VERY, VERY SLOWLY.

The class could try these tests on a number of people to see whether they all get the same result.

Scientific notes
This exercise depends on careful observation and concentration, both of which are important skills for a scientist to acquire.

Science AT1, 3

'On Friday, Fred finally received the result of fifteen years of frustrating scientific research. His future was now assured. He went off to celebrate with his friends, Frank and Fiona.'

Guess my age

Objective
To tell a person's age by using mathematics.

Age range
Nine to eleven.

Group size
Pairs.

What you need
Six coloured square pieces of card bearing numbers, as illustrated.

What to do
Ask the children to place the six cards on the table with the numbered sides uppermost. One child should then shut her eyes or leave the room, while the other turns over any card on which he sees his age (he can pretend to be any age up to 63), and pockets any cards that remain. When his partner returns, she can immediately tell him his age.

Follow-up
When the children know the secret to this trick, can they work out what numbers would appear on a seventh card? What would the new age limit be?

1 3 5 7 9 11
13 15 17 19 21 23
25 27 29 31 33 35
37 39 41 43 45 47
49 51 53 55 57 59
61 63

Red = 1

2 3 6 7 10 11
14 15 18 19 22 23
25 27 30 31 34 35
38 39 42 43 46 47
50 51 54 55 58 59
62 63

Yellow = 2

4 5 6 7 12 13
14 15 20 21 22 23
28 29 30 31 36 37
38 39 44 45 46 47
52 53 54 55 60 61
62 63

Green = 4

8 9 10 11 12 13
14 15 24 25 26 27
28 29 30 31 40 41
42 43 44 45 46 47
56 57 58 59 60 61
62 63

Blue = 8

16 17 18 19 20 21
22 23 24 25 26 27
28 29 30 31 48 49
50 51 52 53 54 55
56 57 58 59 60 61
62 63

White = 16

32 33 34 35 36 37
38 39 40 41 42 43
44 45 46 47 48 49
50 51 52 53 54 55
56 57 58 59 60 61
62 63

Orange = 32

Scientific notes

This activity shows a clever way of using the science of mathematics for fun.

The first number on each card is the key number. The children will need to memorise the following numbers as they relate to the colour of the cards:

Red	=	1
Yellow	=	2
Green	=	4
Blue	=	8
White	=	16
Orange	=	32

The numbers 1, 2, 4, 8, 16, 32 form a geometric progression in which they are increased by a constant factor; that is, each one is multiplied by two. By adding these numbers in a variety of combinations, any number from 1 to 63 can be formed.

The coloured squares have been filled in with the numbers that are needed for each addition. When the victim turns over the coloured squares with his age on, anyone who knows the secret is automatically provided with the key numbers, and by adding together these key numbers they can tell his age.

For example, suppose a person is 53. He will turn over the red, green, white and orange cards. The value of these cards is 1 + 4 + 16 + 32, which comes to 53.

Maths AT1, 2, 3

Upside-down glasses

Objective

To test observation and problem-solving abilities.

Age range

Nine to eleven.

Group size

Pairs or small groups.

What you need

Three glasses, beakers or cups for each group.

What to do

It is probably best to demonstrate this exercise for half the class (or one from each group), and then let them try it out on the others.

Place the three glasses on the table in a row. The two outside glasses (A and C) are upside down, while the centre one (B) is the right way up.

The object of the test is to turn over two glasses at a time and in three moves have them all the right way up.

Take glasses A and B, one in each hand, and turn them over at the same time. Now do the same with glasses A and C, then with A and B. All should now be the correct way up.

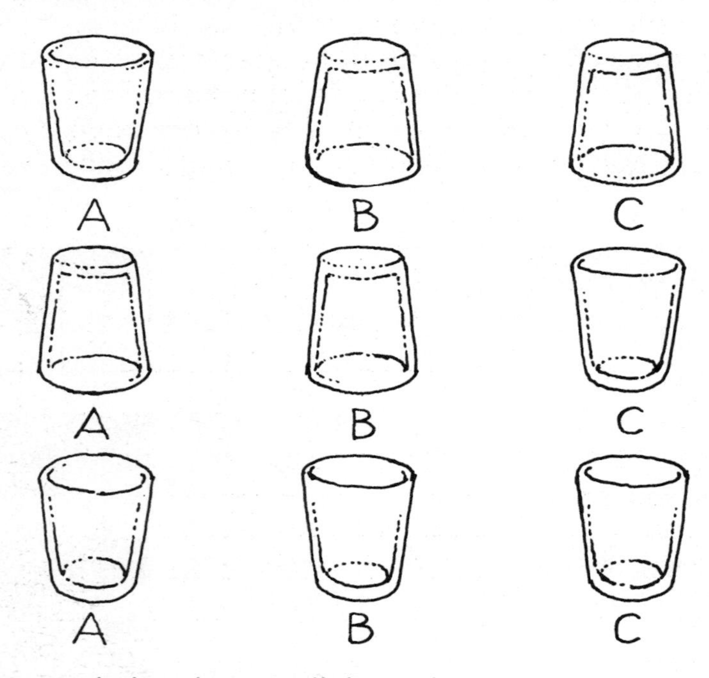

Then, with the glasses all the right way up, casually turn the centre glass upside down and ask someone to repeat what you have just done and get all three glasses the right way up, in three moves. They will not be able to do it.

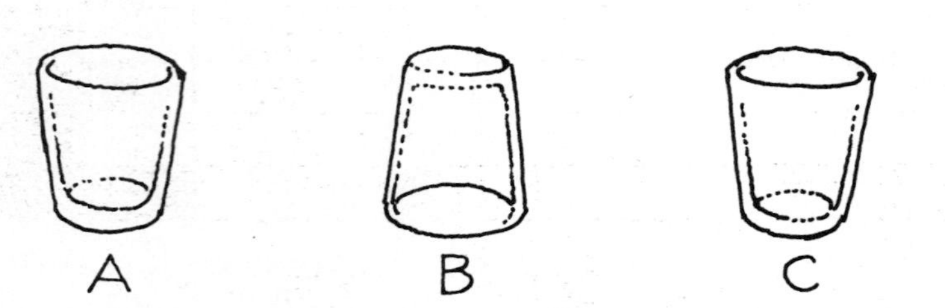

Scientific notes

Once again, observation and concentration skills are required. This trick involves a mathematical principle, but it also relies on the audience not to be very observant.

For the experiment to work, the glasses have to be set up as originally described, with the centre glass the right way up. When you ask the observers to have a go, the chances are that no one will notice that the glasses are set up differently from when you started. No matter how hard they try, it is impossible!

Science AT1, 3

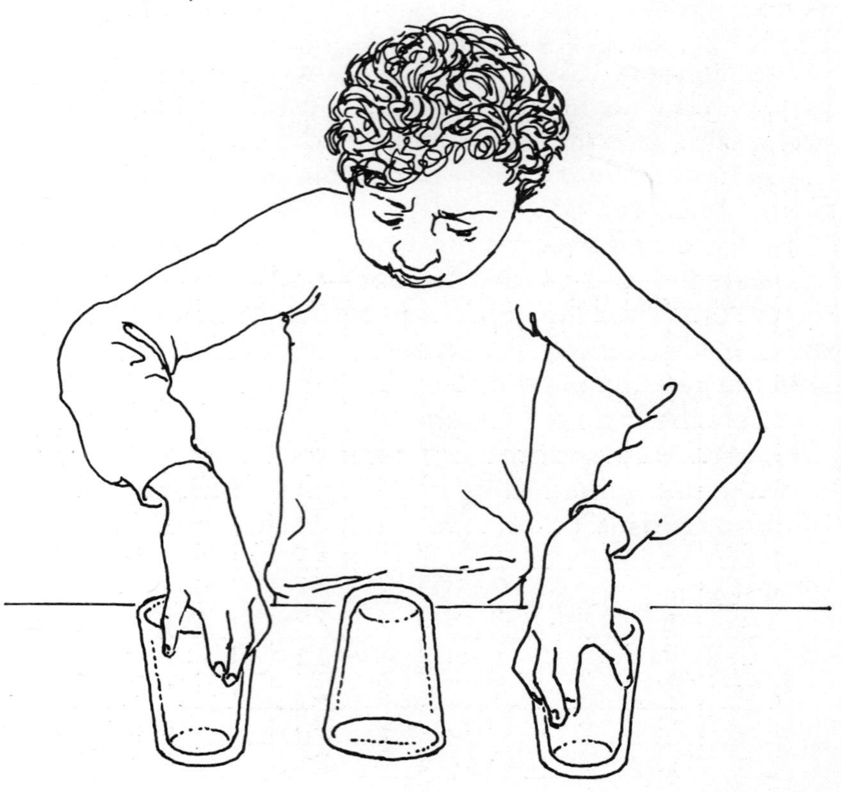

A binary message

Objective
To send a visual message using the binary system.

Age range
Nine to eleven.

Group size
Large groups or the whole class.

What you need
A chart as set out here, showing each letter of the alphabet beside the corresponding Arabic and binary numbers, a copy of photocopiable page 120 for each of the children, centimetre squared paper, coloured felt-tipped pens, different coloured floor tiles or paper squares.

Alphabet	Arabic	Binary numbers	Alphabet	Arabic	Binary numbers
A	1	1	N	14	1 1 1 0
B	2	1 0	O	15	1 1 1 1
C	3	1 1	P	16	1 0 0 0 0
D	4	1 0 0	Q	17	1 0 0 0 1
E	5	1 0 1	R	18	1 0 0 1 0
F	6	1 1 0	S	19	1 0 0 1 1
G	7	1 1 1	T	20	1 0 1 0 0
H	8	1 0 0 0	U	21	1 0 1 0 1
I	9	1 0 0 1	V	22	1 0 1 1 0
J	10	1 0 1 0	W	23	1 0 1 1 1
K	11	1 0 1 1	X	24	1 1 0 0 0
L	12	1 1 0 0	Y	25	1 1 0 0 1
M	13	1 1 0 1	Z	26	1 1 0 1 0

What to do
First, ensure the children understand the binary system and get them to fill in the binary column of the chart.

Then ask them to use the chart to work out a simple message such as 'We are your friends'. Next they could take some centimetre squared paper and, using the binary system, work out the visual pattern. The binary symbol 1 could be represented by a black square and the symbol 0 by a shaded square. It might look like this.

Letter	Binary
W	1 0 1 1 1
E	1 0 1
A	1
R	1 0 0 1 0
E	1 0 1
Y	1 1 0 0 1
O	1 1 1 1
U	1 0 1 0 1
R	1 0 0 1 0
F	1 1 0
R	1 0 0 1 0
I	1 0 0 1
E	1 0 1
N	1 1 1 0
D	1 0 0
S	1 0 0 1 1

Key ■ = 1 ▨ = 0

Follow-up

Coloured floor tiles could be used – for example, black for 1 and white for 0 – and the children could set out a message in the hall and have their friends try to decode it. If you work in a school where you can look down into the playground, the tiled message could be set up outside. Children looking down from their window would have an aerial view and could try to decode the message from there.

Scientific notes

The binary system (base 2) is used by computers and calculators because they use only two symbols, 1 and 0. It is important that children understand this system so that they can use it in their mathematical and scientific studies.

Maths AT1, 2, 3

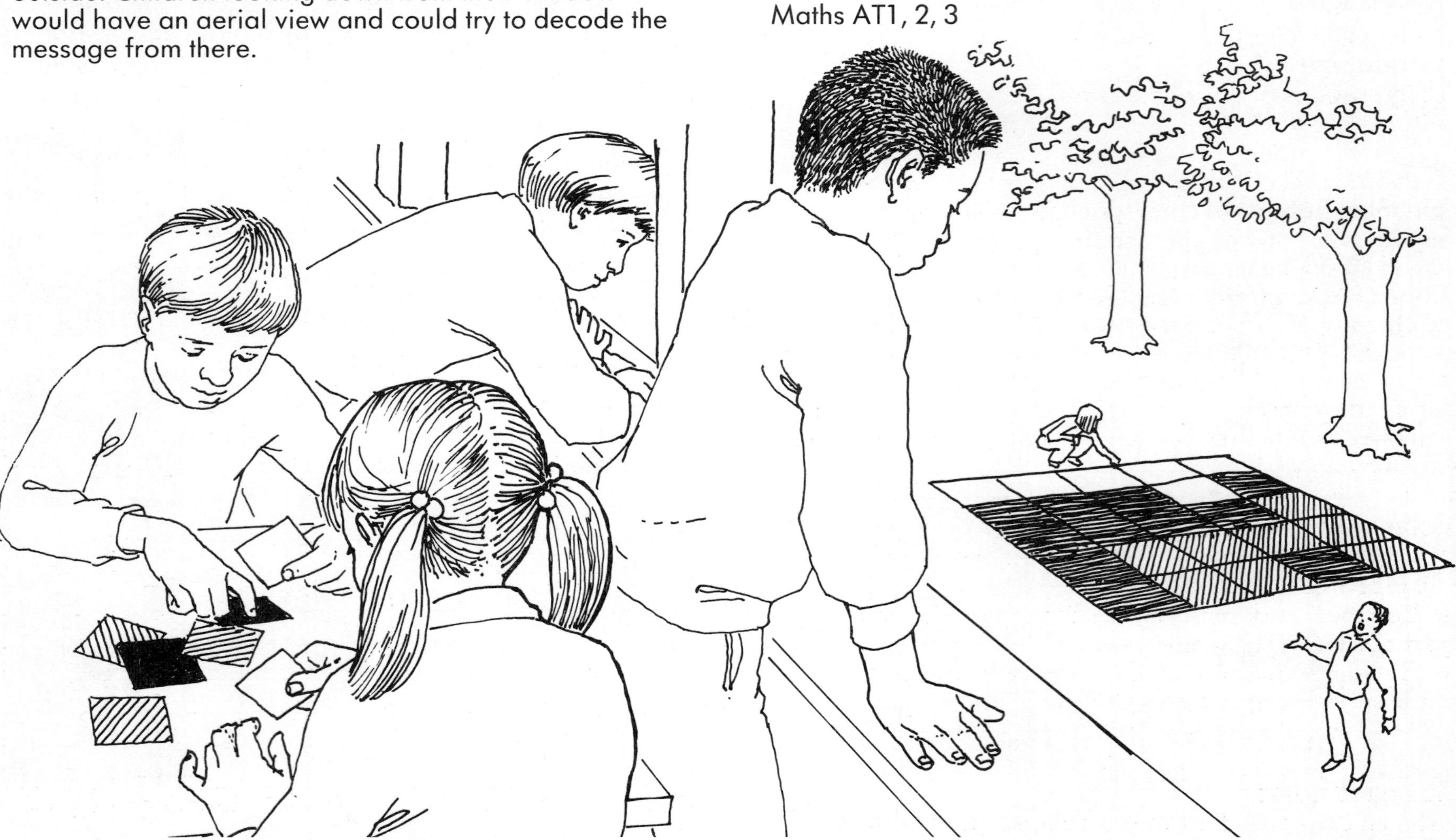

The vanishing rectangle

Objective
To demonstrate how a rectangle seems to disappear by rearranging three pieces of card.

Age range
Nine to eleven.

Group size
Individuals or groups.

What you need
Photocopiable page 121, pieces of card, scissors.

What to do
Copy photocopiable page 121 on to thick paper or card, and give a copy to each child. They will see that there are thirteen rectangles. Ask the children to cut along the dotted lines and rearrange pieces B and C to form a new pattern as shown opposite.

If the children then count the rectangles, they will see that they only have twelve.

Follow-up
- Can the children work out why one rectangle has disappeared?
- Can they work out a similar pattern of their own, perhaps using sixteen rectangles?
- Could the children colour some of the rectangles different colours, and still have the illusion work?

Scientific notes
When pieces B and C are rearranged, parts of some of the rectangles are added to others, thus creating the effect that one has disappeared.

Maths AT10, 11

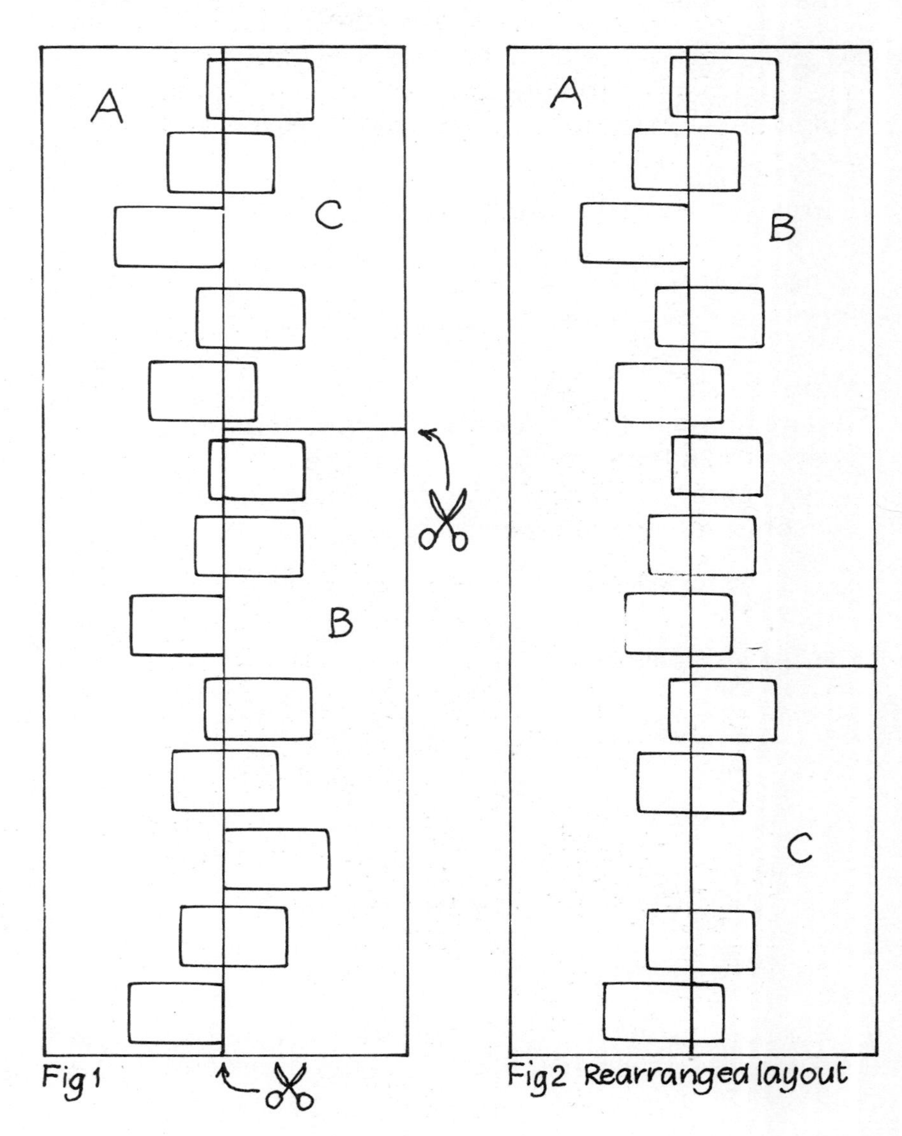

Fig 1 Fig 2 Rearranged layout

Magic square

Objective
To experiment with magic squares.

Age range
Ten to eleven.

Group size
Large groups or the whole class.

What you need
Blank four-by-four squares, pens or pencils.

What to do
The numbers in the square below should be memorised. They remain the same at all times. The letter K stands for 'Key number'. This number is calculated by subtracting 20 from whichever number is given.

K – 1 = the key number minus 1

K + 2 = the key number plus 2

K + 1 = the key number plus 1

K	1	12	7
11	8	K–1	2
5	10	3	K+2
4	K+1	6	9

Ask for any number between, say, 25 and 100. Let us assume that 37 is the number selected; the Key number will be 37 – 20 = 17.

Therefore: K – 1 = 16.
K + 2 = 19.
K + 1 = 18.

As all the other numbers remain the same, the square can now be filled in as shown.

17	1	12	7
11	8	16	2
5	10	3	19
4	18	6	9

This magic square can now be used to find the starting number, 37, in a variety of ways.

Follow-up
Altogether there are 36 different ways of finding the number 37. Here are eleven:
- the four horizontal rows;
- the four columns;
- the two diagonal rows;
- the four corner squares.

Can the children find the other 25? Ask the children to try again, using different numbers between 25 and 100.

Scientific notes
The beauty of this magic square is that you can fill it in for any number between 0 and 100. If a number below 20 is given, you will have to resort to minus numbers.

Maths AT1, 2, 3

Interlocking magic squares

Objective
To use mathematics to appear to perform an amazing calculation and make a successful prediction.

Age range
Ten to eleven.

Group size
Groups or the whole class.

What you need
Copies of photocopiable page 122; two small pieces of card, one large enough to cover four squares, and one to cover five squares.

What to do
One member of each group should cover any four squares with the small card. Another group member can immediately call out the total of the four squares.

To achieve this feat, they simply move diagonally outwards from any corner of the group of numbers covered, and stop at the second square they reach. Then they should mentally subtract its number from 65. This will give them the total of the four numbers covered by the small square piece of card.

For example, suppose squares 13, 5, 19 and 6 are covered, totalling 43. The second square reached moving away diagonally in any direction is 22. This number subtracted from 65 gives 43.

24	11	3	20	7	24	11	3	20	7
5	17	9	21	13	5	17	9	21	13
6	23	15	2	19	6	23	15	2	19
12	4	16	8	25	12	4	16	8	25
18	10	22	14	1	18	10	22	14	1
24	11	3	20	7	24	11	3	20	7
5	17	9	21	13	5	17	9	21	13
6	23	15	2	19	6	23	15	2	19
12	4	16	8	25	12	4	16	8	25
18	10	22	14	1	18	10	22	14	1

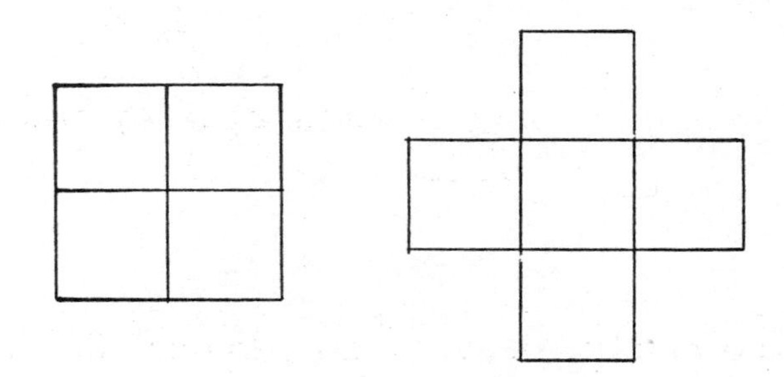

Follow-up

- If someone covers any five numbers with the cross-shaped piece of card, anyone who knows the secret can immediately announce the total of the five squares as 65, since when any five numbers are covered in this way, they will always total 65.
- Can the children make up a similar 100 square by changing the numbers; for example, by adding three to each number? Now they can see if they can work out the total of the four covered squares. What would be the total of five covered squares?

Scientific notes

Each quarter of the 100 square is made up of the numbers 1–25 arranged in exactly the same way. These are in fact 'magic squares' where all the rows, horizontal, vertical and diagonal, add up to 65. Putting the four squares together produces a large interlocking magic square.

Maths AT1, 2, 3

Magical dominoes

Objective

To demonstrate how the science of mathematics can bestow an apparent ability to predict the result of a game of chance.

Age range

Nine to eleven.

Group size

Pairs or small groups.

What you need

A full set of dominoes for each group, pieces of paper, pencils or pens.

What to do

Before the start of the game, one person from each group must be told to remove a domino secretly, making sure it is not a double.

Let us suppose the domino removed is the 5/3; the player should write these numbers on a piece of paper as a prediction of the resulting end numbers.

The group can then play a game of dominoes. When the game has been completed, the two end numbers should be those predicted, in this case five and three. When the prediction is opened it will seem as though the result of a game of chance has been predicted.

Follow-up

Can the class say whether this still works if some of the pieces remain unused at the end of the game?

Scientific notes

The reason this works is that if the game of dominoes is played to a finish with every piece used up, the set will complete a full circuit. The domino that is secretly removed beforehand is the one needed to complete the circuit, so the numbers on that domino are the ones that will be unmatched at the end.

Maths AT1, 2, 3

Visual deceptions

We rely upon our sense of sight for most of our daily activities. To imagine what it is like to be deprived of your vision, try moving around your home with your eyes shut. You will find it extremely difficult, despite being in familiar surroundings.

Even with your eyes open, it is possible to be visually deceived. Children always find tricks that are visually deceptive great fun, and the experiments in this section can be a good introduction to work aimed at increasing self-awareness.

The shadow pictures can lead the children on to doing shadow tricks and shadow plays, culminating with further work on this fascinating subject.

Optical illusions are always fun, and children like looking at them. They can be a good lead-in to topics on subjects such as 'Colour' or 'Our senses'.

Two excellent packs of cards, *Can you believe your eyes* and *More illusions and visual oddities*, have been distributed by Intercol (1a Camden Walk, Islington Green, London N1 8DY). They are obtainable from good stationers.

Optical illusions have been appearing in books and magazines for a great many years. Recently an excellent book, *Take a a closer look*, by Keith Kay (Brinbo Books) has made its appearance. Read the title again! It's not a printing error. This book contains some optical illusions from that publication on photocopiable pages 123 to 126, which may be reproduced for classroom purposes.

Magical curves

Objective
To create an optical illusion with two cut-out curves which are exactly the same size.

Age range
Five to eight.

Group size
The whole class, pairs or individuals.

What you need
Pieces of A4 size card, coloured felt-tipped pens, scissors.

What to do
On the card, draw larger versions of the curves shown below. Each child will need both A and B. The two curves must be exactly the same size.

Ask the children to cut out the two curves and colour each a different colour. Younger children may need help with the cutting.

The children should now place the cut-outs on the table, one above the other, as shown below. The curve at the bottom will look larger.

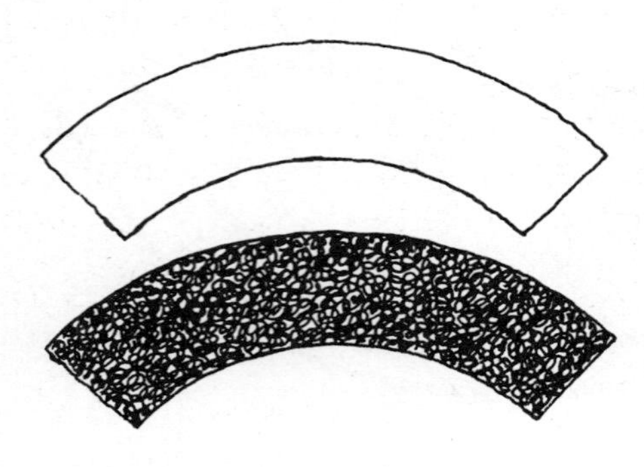

Follow-up
Ask the children to try to explain why the bottom curve looks larger.

For fun, they can place the curves as shown below, and cut off the 'extra bit' that appears to be on the bottom curve. Then they should measure one against the other to see whether they are the same size.

Scientific notes
Whenever one curve is placed above the other the one at the bottom will always appear to be larger, because the upper edge of the lower cut-out is substantially longer than the lower edge of the upper cut-out.

Science AT1, 2

A hole in your hand

Objective
To show what happens when both eyes focus on different objects at the same time, and when we focus on something using only one eye.

Age range
Five to eleven.

Group size
Individuals.

What you need
Sheets of paper, small cardboard tubes, pencils.

What to do
If you do not have any cardboard tubes, ask the children to roll a sheet of paper into a tube.

Instruct the children to put one end of the tube to their right eye and to hold their left hand with the palm towards them, against the tube. *Both eyes must be kept open*. It will appear that there is a hole in the left hand.

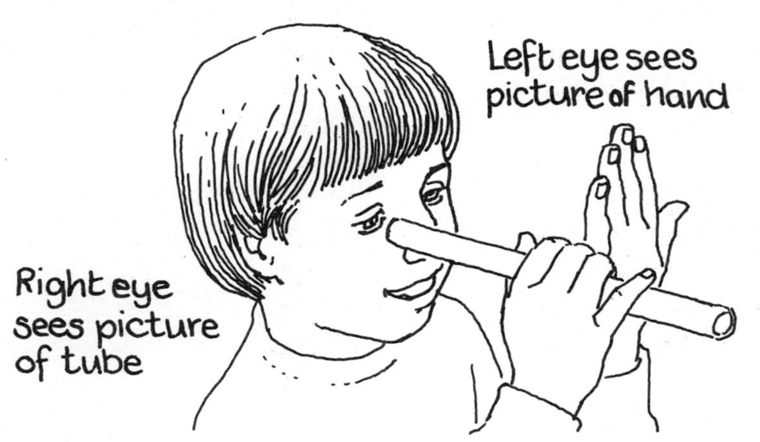

Follow-up
The children should draw a dot on a piece of paper and put it on the table in front of them. Holding a pencil in one hand and covering one eye with the other hand they must try to touch the dot *quickly* with the pencil. Next they can hold the pencil in the other hand and cover the other eye, and then try with both eyes open.

Scientific notes
This optical illusion is a result of binocular vision. One eye looks through the tube and the other looks at the hand. The two views blend together to give the illusion of a hole in the hand. The follow-up shows how hard it is to judge distances with one eye.

Science AT1, 2, 15

Disappearing stamp

Objective
To demonstrate how something can seem to vanish because of the phenomenon of refraction.

Age range
Eight to eleven.

Group size
Individuals or pairs.

What you need
Postage stamps (or similar small objects), clear glasses full of water, pieces of card, pencils.

What to do
Ask the children to place a postage stamp on a table and cover it with a glass of water. They should then cover the glass with the card. Now, if they look into the glass from any angle, the stamp is completely invisible.

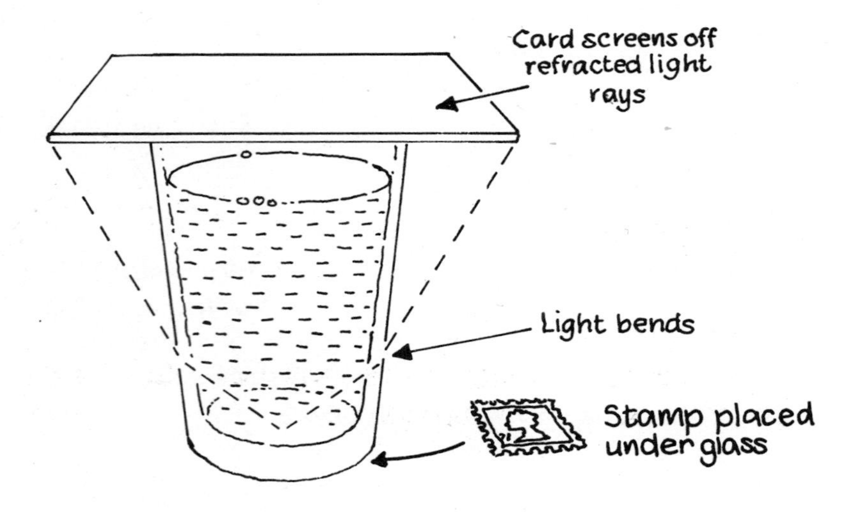

Follow-up
If the children place a pencil in the glass of water, they will see that the pencil appears to bend.

Scientific notes
Light will travel through transparent substances such as water, air and glass. When the light rays pass from one substance to another (of different densities) they appear to bend at the point where the two substances meet. This is called 'refraction'.

The dotted lines show how the light rays are refracted upwards when they pass out from the stamp from water to air, and how they strike the underside of the card. Because the card screens off all refracted rays, there is no angle from which the stamp can be seen.

Science AT1, 2, 15

Amazing lunch bag

Objectives
To insert needles into a bag of water without leakage, and to observe effects caused by refraction.

Age range
Eight to eleven.

Group size
Pairs.

What you need
Some knitting needles, a supply of clear plastic lunch or freezer bags, water, a white sheet of paper, newspaper.

What to do
Very carefully, the children should pour water into the bag until it is *just under half full*. They should then twist the top of the bag a little.

Holding the bag in one hand, the children can now quickly stick a knitting needle into the bag, so that it protrudes from the other side. If this is done correctly, the water will stay in the bag.

The children may need to practise a few times before they can do it without losing any water. The secret is to stick the needle into the bag at just the right speed and with no hesitation.

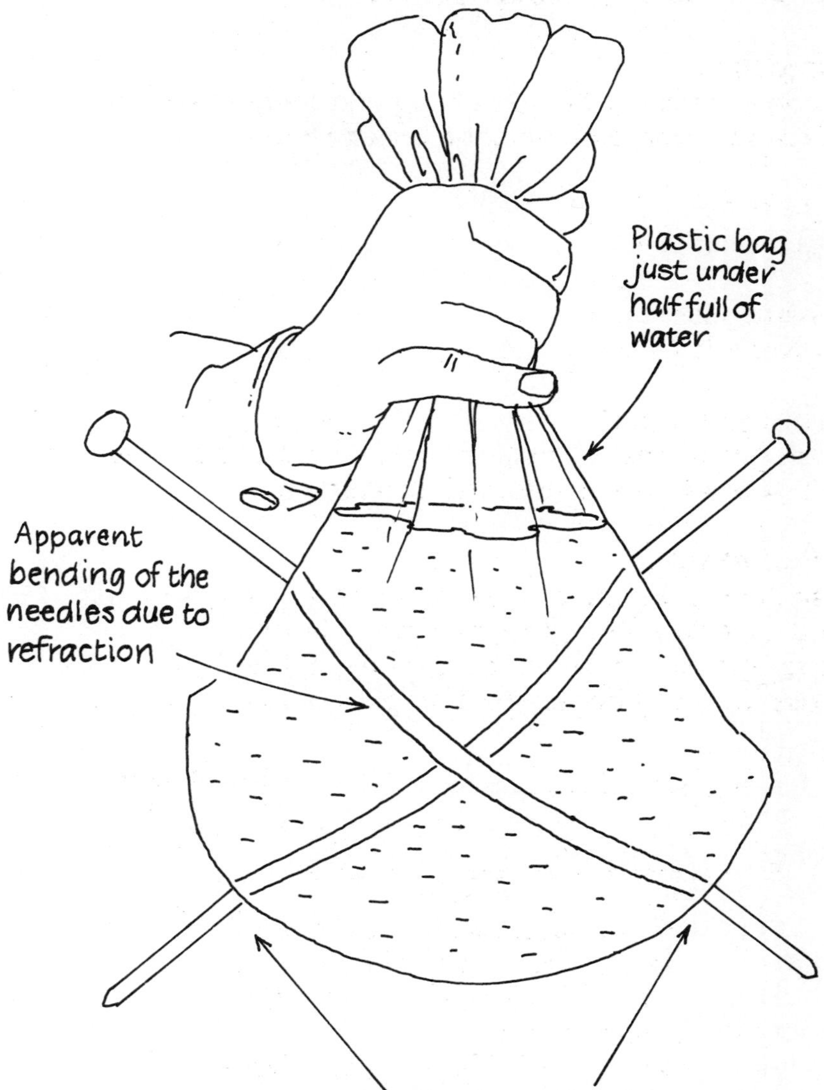

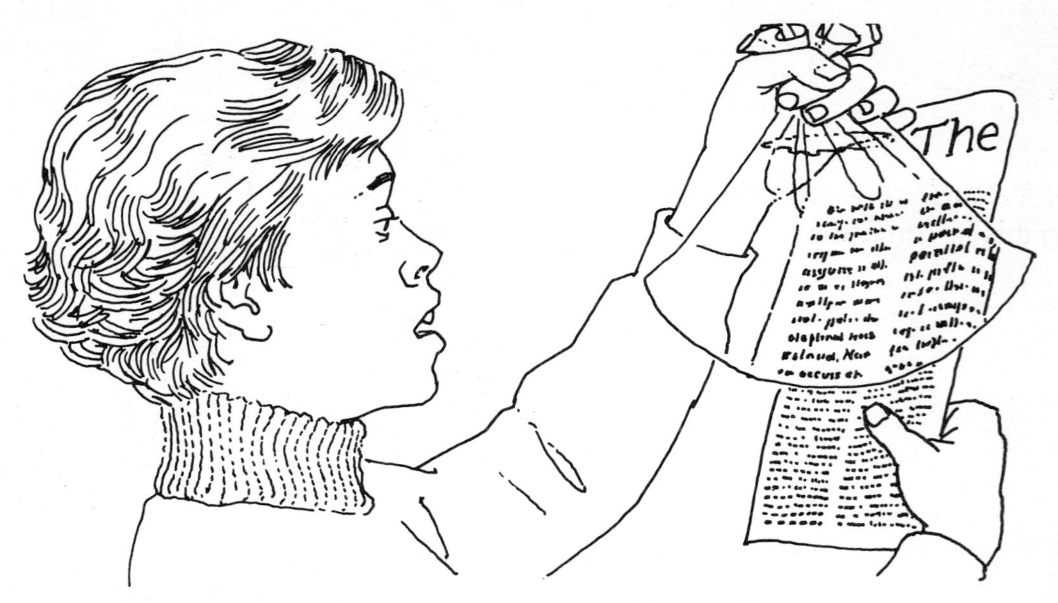

Follow-up

Tell the children to hold the bag up to the light and look at it. Depending upon the angle at which they are viewing the bag, the part of the needle inside the bag will appear to bend downwards, bend upwards, double in size or multiply.

Ask the children to see how many needles can be stuck into the bag without losing any water. What optical illusions do they see now when they look at the bag from different angles?

If the children half-fill another bag or a glass or bottle with water, and hold part of a newspaper behind it, what do they see? Are some of the words and pictures magnified?

Holding the bag up to very bright sunlight, with something white behind it, can the children see some of the colours of the rainbow? They can try this also in a darkened room; instead of sunlight a torch can be shone on the bag of water.

Scientific notes

The pressure of the water inside the bag forces the plastic film to form a watertight seal around the needle. However, for this to work, the hole formed should be more or less the same size as the needle. If it is any larger, the bag will leak water. The apparent bending of the needles inside the bag is caused by refraction – the bending of light rays.

In the follow-up activities, the magnification of the words or pictures in the newspaper is again caused by the bending of light rays as they go through the water.

If the colours of the rainbow are visible, this is also caused by refraction. The colours of the spectrum that make up white light are separated as they pass through the water because the various colours are bent differently; violet is bent the most and red the least. The different colours therefore strike the white background at different places.

Science AT1, 2, 15

Shadow pictures

Objectives
To demonstrate how a shadow is formed and to create some shadow pictures using this information.

Age range
Ten to eleven.

Group size
Small groups or individuals.

What you need
Strong torches or desk lamps, a darkened room, a white wall or screen, photocopiable pages 127 to 128.

What to do
One child from each group should shine a torch on the white wall or, if a desk lamp is used, it can be positioned on a table so that its light falls on the wall.

The children should move their hands up and down in the light, making a shadow on the wall. Ask them to stand close to the light and then move further away, and say what they notice about the size of the shadow.

On pages 127 to 128 there are shadow pictures of some animals for the children to try. They will need a little practice at first. When making the animals the children should always look at the shadows on the wall, rather than at their hands. Only when they think the picture is correct should they look at their hands to take note of the position of their fingers.

Follow-up
When the children can do the hand shadows competently, they can present them to the whole class or school, making use of the school screen if there is one. This will involve finding out how to present shadow puppets and plays.

Scientific notes
Light passes through transparent substances like glass or water. When it meets an opaque substance such as a tree, house or person, it cannot pass through. Because light travels in a straight line and does not go round corners, a shadow is produced when it meets one of these opaque objects.

The shadows in the experiment are created because the light from the torch or lamp cannot penetrate a hand, which is opaque.

If the hand is near to the lamp it tends to block out a lot of light, so the shadow will be large. When the hand is further away from the lamp, less light is blocked out, so the hand shadow will be very much smaller.

Science AT1, 2, 15

Magical letters

Objective
To show how some letters of the alphabet remain the same when viewed upside down in a mirror.

Age range
Eight to eleven.

Group size
Individuals or pairs.

What you need
Pieces of paper, felt-tipped pens, mirrors, alphabet cards (capital letters).

What to do
Ask the children to write the words 'A GREAT CHOICE' in capital letters on a piece of paper. If they hold it in front of a mirror, the letters will appear to be back to front. Turn the paper upside down and, surprisingly, the word 'CHOICE' remains the same, while the words 'A GREAT' do not.

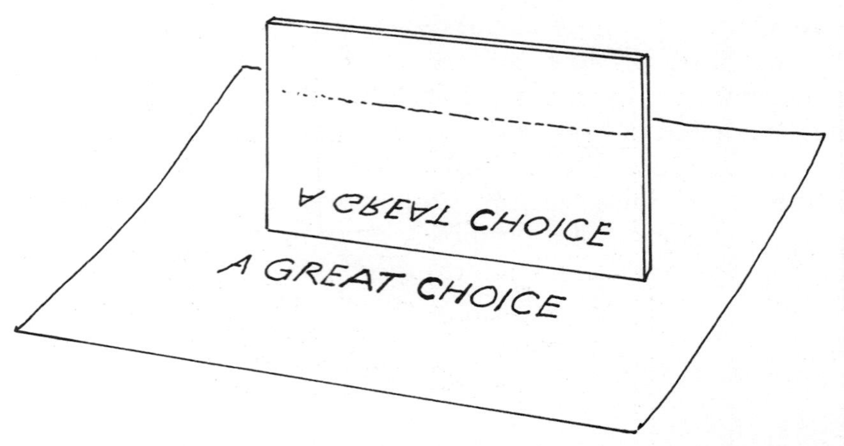

Follow-up

Get the children to print the letters of the alphabet in capital letters on a piece of paper. If they hold them upside down in front of a mirror, they will see that some letters remain the same, while others do not. Ask them to make a list of the letters that are still the same. Using these letters, let them write a list of all the words they can make (they are allowed to use the same letter more than once). When the list is complete the children can hold it upside down in front of a mirror and should still be able to read the words. It may be easier to use the alphabet cards instead of writing the words down.

Scientific notes

Mirrors are used to reflect light rays. In the phrase 'A GREAT CHOICE', the word CHOICE does not appear to turn upside down and can still be read in the normal manner, because the letters are all symmetrical about a horizontal line, and therefore the word looks the same either way up.

The letters K O B C D E H I X all react in the same way.

Science AT1, 2, 15

Mixed bag

Here is a miscellany of activities, hence the title. How does a boomerang work? What is inertia? How can a plastic comb alter the flow of water from a kitchen tap? How can you hear church bells by banging a spoon on a chair?

These are just four of the questions that can be answered by trying the experiments in this section.

Each one illustrates a scientific principle and, if the experiments are carried out carefully, they all work!

Boomerang card

Objective
To show how the spin of a boomerang makes it return to you.

Age range
Nine to eleven.

Group size
Individuals or pairs.

What you need
An old pack of cards, pencils, a pair of scissors.

What to do
Each child should take one of the playing cards and cut an L-shaped boomerang, making sure that the ends are rounded.

The cardboard boomerang should be placed on the card case, as shown in the illustration. Now the children can strike the end of the boomerang with the pencil. The boomerang should spin forwards and upwards before returning.

A little practice will be needed to get the right angle at which to hold the card case and to strike the boomerang with the pencil with the right amount of force.

Follow-up

The children can make a four-sided boomerang (rotor) from a playing card and repeat the first exercise. They can try the same thing with a three-sided boomerang.

Scientific notes

Things that are streamlined in shape travel through the air easily. The more edges or angles they have, the more air resistance there is. The spin of the boomerang is an essential part of its working. It converts the boomerang into a gyroscope. As long as it spins, it will fly through the air and return to the thrower. The angle at which the card case is held is important.

A slight bend in the tip of the boomerang will give it a large orbit, while a large bend will give it a smaller orbit.

Science AT1, 10

Good vibrations

Objective
To show how sound is produced by vibrations.

Age range
Five to eleven.

Group size
Individuals.

What you need
Spoons, pieces of string about 1½ metres in length, tables or chairs.

What to do
Ask the children to tie a spoon to the centre of the string. They should wrap one end of the string around the index finger of the left hand, the other end around the index finger of the right hand, and then put the tips of both fingers into their ears. Now if they bend forward and allow the spoon to strike against the chair, they will hear a sound like chiming bells.

Follow-up
Let the children try this experiment with other items such as forks or wire coat-hangers.

Scientific notes
The sound is produced by the vibrations of the spoon. The sound waves are transmitted to the eardrums via the string and fingers.

Science AT1, 14

High-speed monorail

Objective
To demonstrate how stored-up energy in an elastic band will make a balsa train shoot along a length of string.

Age range
Nine to eleven.

Group size
Large groups.

What you need
Pieces of balsa-wood shaped and painted to look like a high-speed train, long pieces of string, beads, propellers, elastic bands, wire coat-hangers, bradawl, pliers, wire cutters.

What to do
The children should, under close supervision, cut two long pieces and one small piece of wire from the coat-hanger. To make the train go, first use a bradawl to make a hole about 5cm from each end. Put the long pieces of wire through the holes, hooking the ends over. Hang the train from the string, and assemble the other piece of wire, beads, propeller and elastic band as illustrated.

If the children now wind up the elastic band by turning the propeller and let go, they can watch the train shoot off.

Follow-up
- What will happen if the children vary the number of twists given to the elastic band?
- Will the thickness and length of the elastic band make any difference?

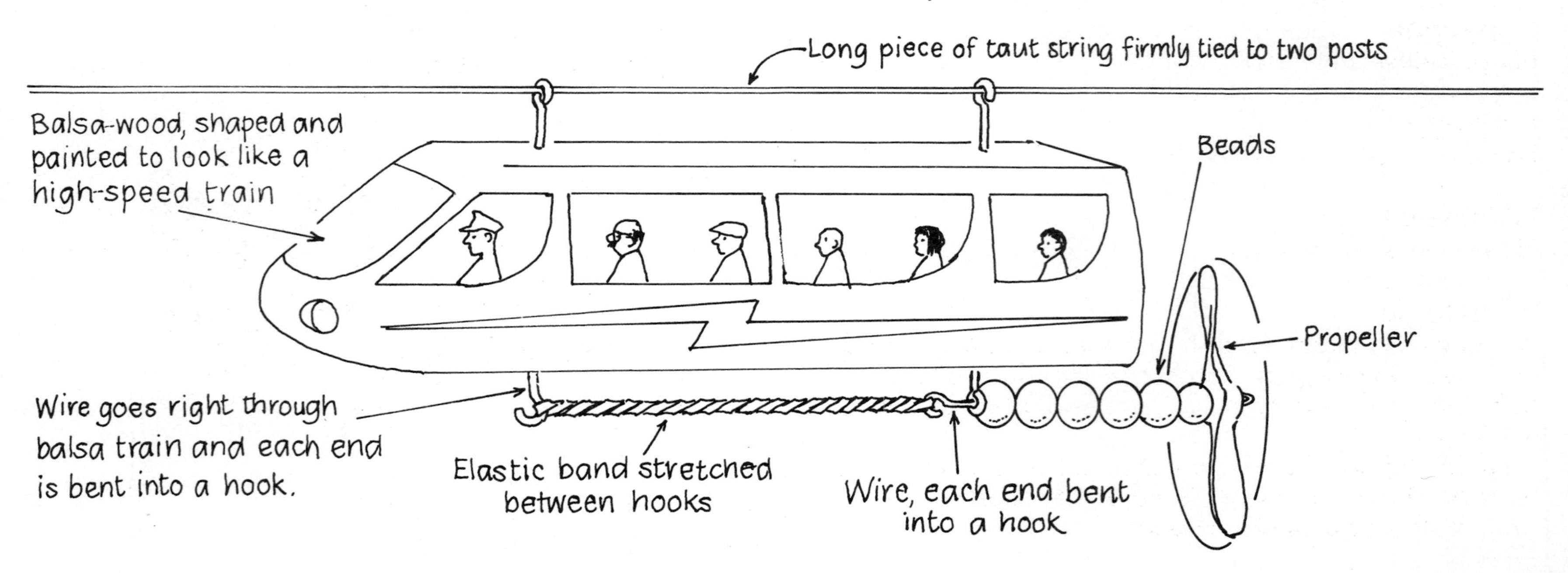

• Can the children think of any other experiments where the energy stored in an elastic band is used?

Scientific notes

As the propeller is turned, the elastic band is twisted and tightened. As the elastic band unwinds it releases the energy stored in the twisted elastic, causing the propeller to spin. This makes the train move.

Science AT1, 10, 13

Headstrong

Objective

To demonstrate apparent strength.

Age range

Nine to eleven.

Group size

Pairs.

What you need

No special equipment.

What to do

Ask one child in each pair to put her hand on her head and press downwards. Another child should take hold of her forearm and try to pull her hand upwards and off her head.

No matter how hard he tries, the other child will fail in his task. The child with her hand on her head apparently has unlimited strength.

Follow-up

• Ask the smallest and the largest child in the class to try the experiment. Does it still work?
• Instead of pressing their hands on to their heads, ask the children to use just their extended fingertips. What happens?

Scientific notes

The direction of the forces involved means that when one child tries to lift up the forearm of the other, he is in fact having to lift the entire body of the other child. It is impossible to do this in this manner!

Science AT1, 10

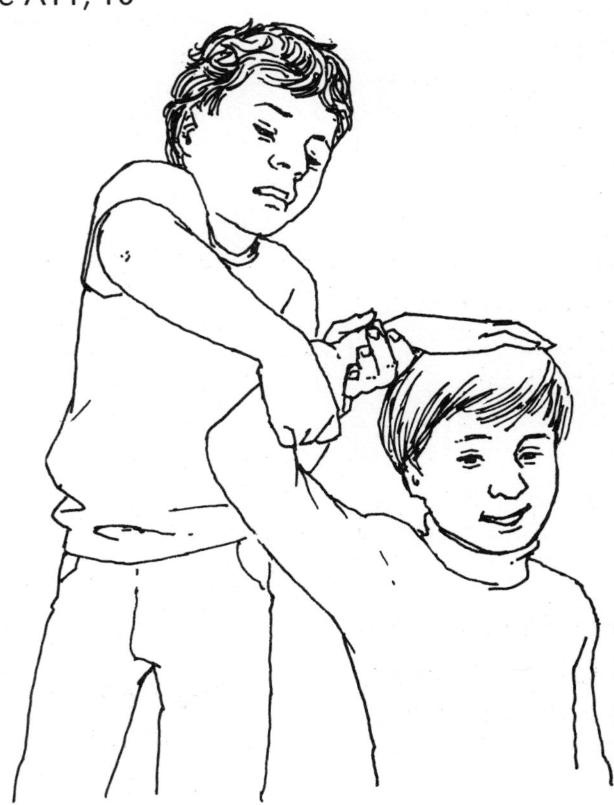

It's a corker

Objective
To demonstrate how a cork, when dropped on a table, can be made to land on its end.

Age range
Seven to eleven.

Group size
Individuals or small groups.

What you need
A cork and a table.

What to do
Hand the cork to a child and ask him to drop it on to the table so that it will stand on its end. Unless he is lucky, the cork will probably land on its side.

When you do it, drop the cork so that it hits the table on its side. It will bounce, and should then stand upright.

Follow-up
- Ask the children to try dropping the cork from different heights. Does it make any difference?
- Let the children try bouncing other items, like pen tops, tops of adhesive stick containers, and so on. If a piece of Blu-Tack is put inside at one end as a weight, does it make any difference?

Scientific notes
The cork will always bounce because of its lightness. When it lands on its side, it will often bounce and finish on its end. You will need to practise this to ascertain the exact distance to drop the cork. It is this distance that governs the force of the bounce in relation to the centre of gravity of the cork. A bounce which is much less forceful than the drop will be needed to enable the cork to land on its end.

Science AT1, 10

A magnetic puzzle

Objective
To remove some paper clips and drawing pins from a glass of water without pouring out or reaching into the water.

Age range
Seven to eleven.

Group size
Pairs or small groups.

What you need
Tumblers of water, drawing pins, paper-clips, magnets.

What to do
Let one child put some drawing pins and paper-clips in the tumbler of water, and ask someone to remove the paper-clips and drawing pins without reaching into the water or pouring any out.

When they can't do it, the child should produce the magnet and place it on the outside of the tumbler next to the paper-clips and drawing pins. The magnet will attract the metal items through the glass, and the child can then slide them up the inside of the glass. When they reach the top of the tumbler the paper-clips and pins will still cling to the magnet, and can be lifted up out of the way.

Follow-up
- Ask the children to find out if this experiment will work with a tin can instead of a glass of water.
- Let them try using other containers of different thicknesses, made of glass, wood, plastic, china and aluminium.

Scientific notes
The magnetic force goes through the glass (or any other non-magnetic material that is not too thick) and attracts the paper-clips and drawing pins.

Science AT1, 11

Hit the stack

Objective
To demonstrate the principle of inertia.

Age range
Nine to eleven.

Group size
Small groups.

What you need
Some draught pieces (about ten for each group), rulers, a smooth table surface.

What to do
The children should stack all the draught pieces as shown in the first illustration.

They can then hold one end of the ruler, keeping it flat against the table surface, with the other end at point A in the illustration, to the left of the draught pieces. If they move the ruler sharply to the right and hit the bottom draught piece, allowing the ruler to carry on through its momentum so that it finishes at point B, the bottom draught piece should move from under the stack and leave the column of draught pieces still standing. It may take some practice.

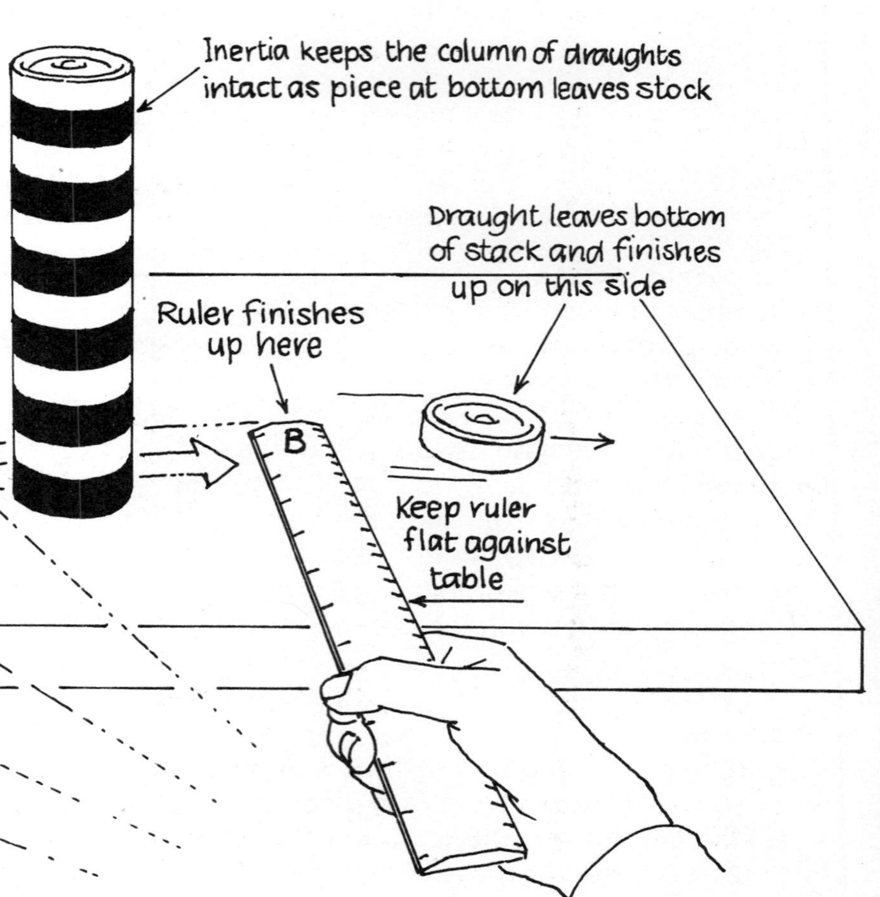

Follow-up

When the children can do this every time, get them to rebuild the stack of draught pieces, ensuring that they use alternate colours (black, white, black, and so on).

After making the initial hit from point A to point B, they should make the second from B to A and so on. If this is done correctly they will end up with one set of colours to the right and one to the left. This is quite difficult to do and will need some practice.

For another experiment that is a little easier, ask the children to set up the pieces again as in the first experiment. Taking it in turns, let them hold one of the draught pieces as shown in the second illustration. If they press the forefinger down on the edge of this draught it will shoot forward towards the stack. It will hit the piece second from the bottom, causing it to leave the column. The remaining pieces will remain intact.

Scientific notes

In these two experiments, the weight of the two columns of draught pieces keep the stacks intact as the pieces at the bottom are knocked away. This is called inertia; that is, the tendency of a body to stay as it is, either at rest or travelling at a steady speed.

Science AT1, 10

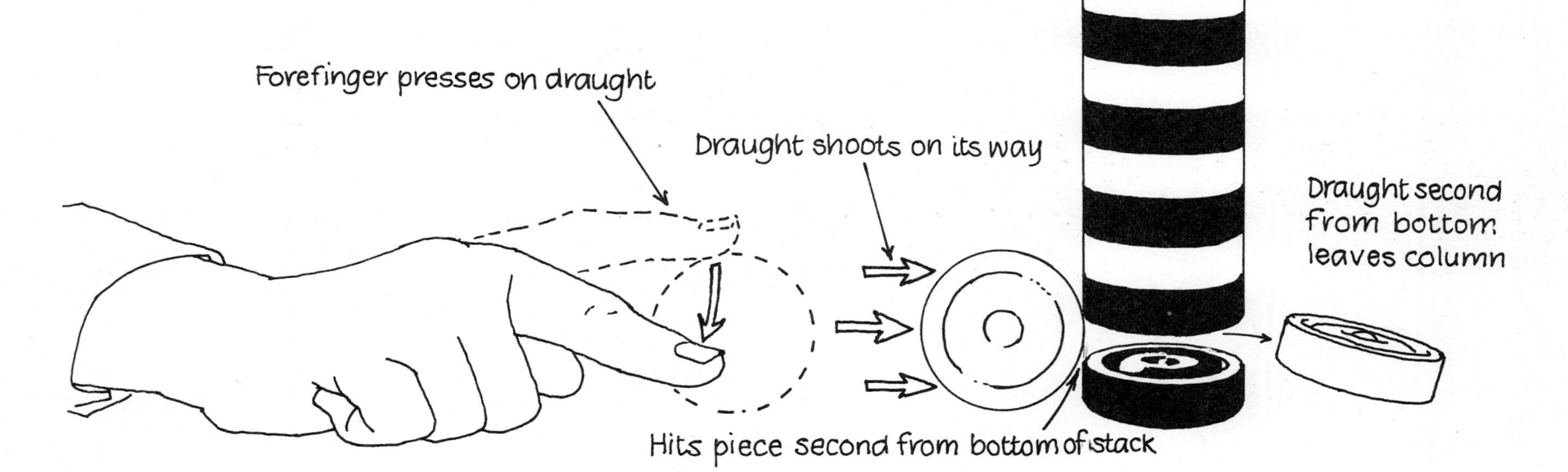

Electrostatic comb

Objective
To show how a comb charged with static electricity can alter the flow of a thin stream of water.

Age range
Seven to eleven.

Group size
Individuals or pairs.

What you need
Combs, table tennis balls, a tap with running water.

What to do
This experiment is best done on a cold, *dry* day. Turn on the cold water tap so that a very thin stream of water flows from it.

The children should rub a plastic comb briskly on a woollen jumper and then hold it as near as possible to the stream of water.

The water will change its course, because it has become attracted by the comb.

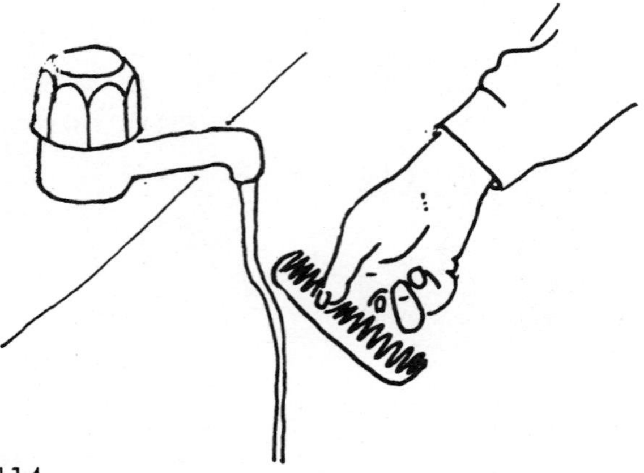

Follow-up
If the children place a table tennis ball on a table, rub the comb on the jumper and move it around the ball in circles, the table tennis ball will follow the comb.

Let them experiment to see whether other items can be used instead of a comb.

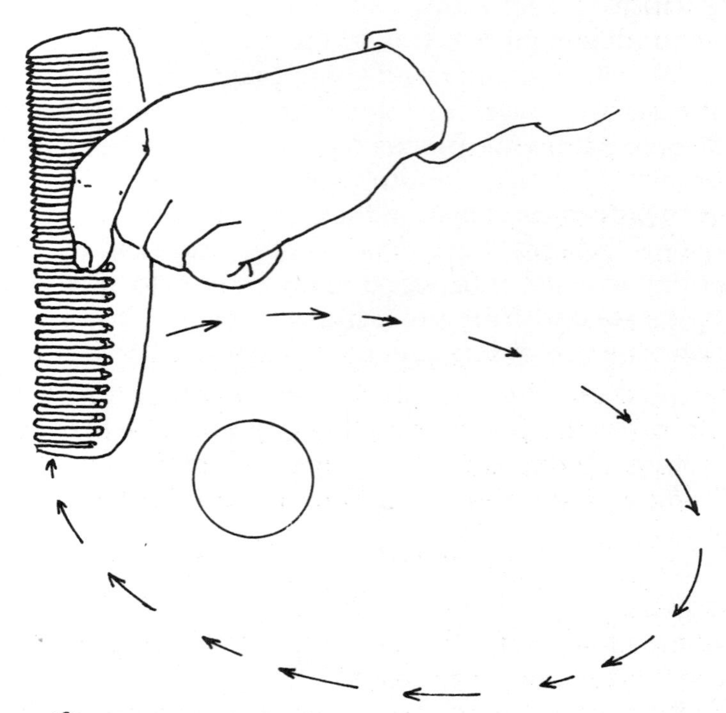

Scientific notes
Rubbing the comb on a woollen jumper charges it with static electricity; the comb becomes a charged object. A charged object placed near an uncharged object creates an opposite charge on the near side of the uncharged object. Thus the uncharged stream of water and the table tennis balls become attracted by the comb.

Science AT1, 11

Electrostatic news

Objective
To demonstrate how static electricity can cause a sheet of newspaper to adhere to a wall.

Age range
Seven to eleven.

Group size
Small groups or pairs.

What you need
Sheets of newspaper, pencils.

What to do
Ask the children to hold a small sheet of newspaper against a wall with one hand. With the other hand, they should press the pencil longways against the sheet and rub it hard up and down a number of times. Then they can remove their hands; the paper should adhere to the wall.

Follow-up
- Let the children try this experiment with paper of different sizes and thicknesses.
- Let them try rubbing the paper against a partner's back instead of the wall.

Scientific notes
The rubbing generates static electricity in the piece of newspaper. This causes it to stick to uncharged surfaces. The experiment will work best in cool, dry weather.

Science AT1, 11

See-sawing candle

Objective
To demonstrate how gravity enables a candle to see-saw for a lengthy period of time.

Age range
Nine to eleven.

Group size
Pairs or small groups.

What you need
Candles, needles, tumblers, metal trays, matches.

What to do
Under close supervision, let the children cut away some of the wax at the end of a candle so that the wick is exposed.

Next, starting at one end of the candle, they should make marks at centimetre intervals, and then mark the exact centre of the candle. They should push a needle right through the centre so that it protrudes from both sides.

Ask them to place two tumblers on a tray and rest the ends of the needle on them so that the candle resembles a see-saw in a balanced position. If they light the wick first at one end of the candle and then at the other, after a short while a drop of candle wax will drip on to the tray from one of the ends. When this happens the other end will tip, just like a see-saw. This action will repeat itself, first one end, then the other.

Follow-up
The children can time the action and see how long it takes to burn away a centimetre from each end.

- Is the burning consistent throughout?
- Does the candle see-saw behave in exactly the same way all the time?

Scientific notes
It is important that the candle is perfectly balanced at the outset. As wax drips from the end of the candle lit first, that side becomes lighter than the other. Gravity then pulls down the heavy end, which causes it to drip a larger amount of wax. This then makes that end lighter, so it goes up, while the other end goes down. This see-saw action will go on for quite some time.

Science AT1, 10

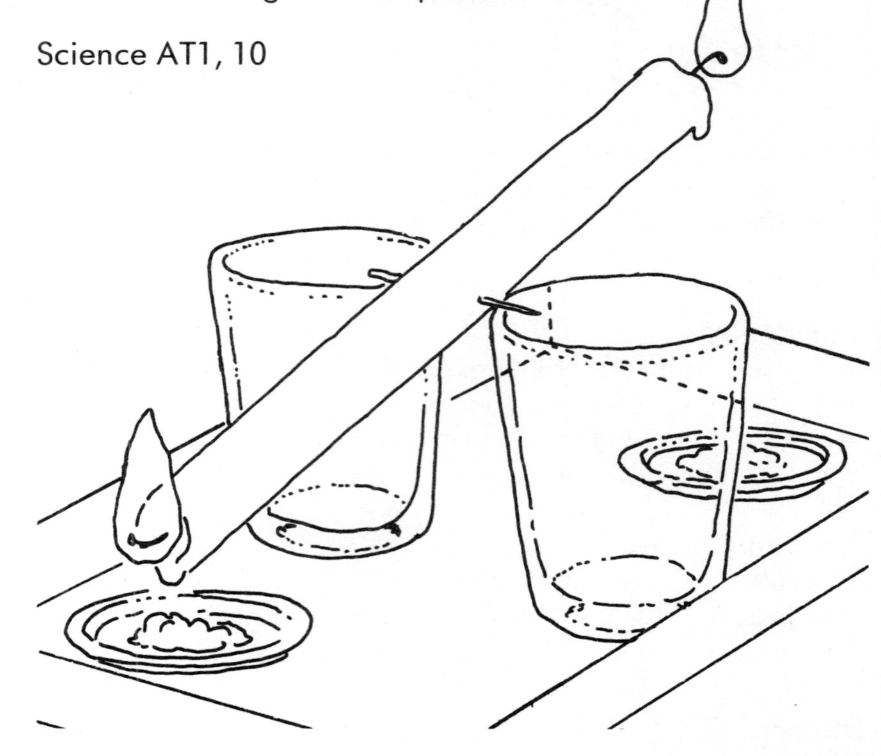

Reproducible material

Jumping clown, see page 59

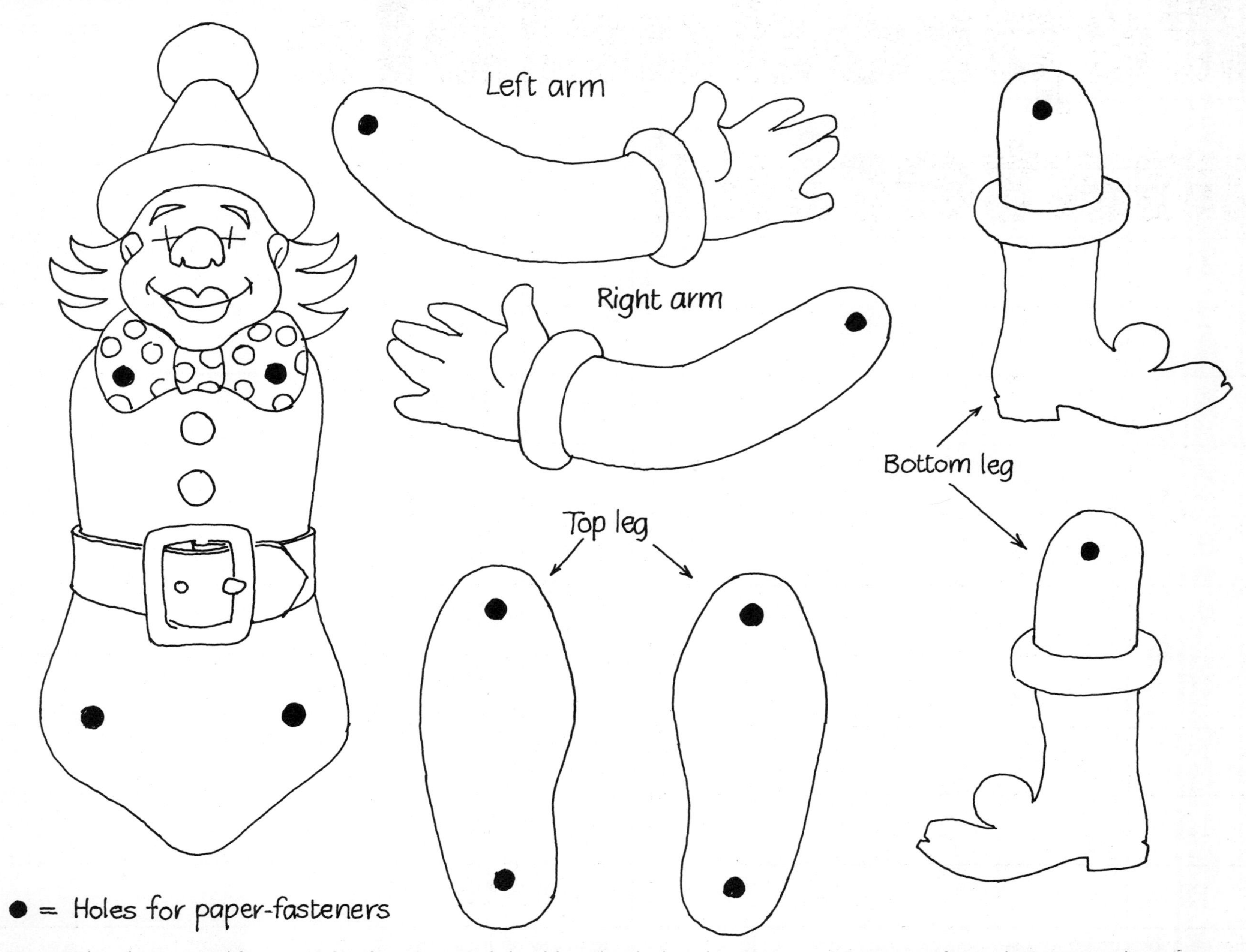

A binary message, see page 87

Alphabet	Arabic	Binary numbers
A	1	
B	2	
C	3	
D	4	
E	5	
F	6	
G	7	
H	8	
I	9	
J	10	
K	11	
L	12	
M	13	

Alphabet	Arabic	Binary numbers
N	14	
O	15	
P	16	
Q	17	
R	18	
S	19	
T	20	
U	21	
V	22	
W	23	
X	24	
Y	25	
Z	26	

Vanishing rectangle, see page 89

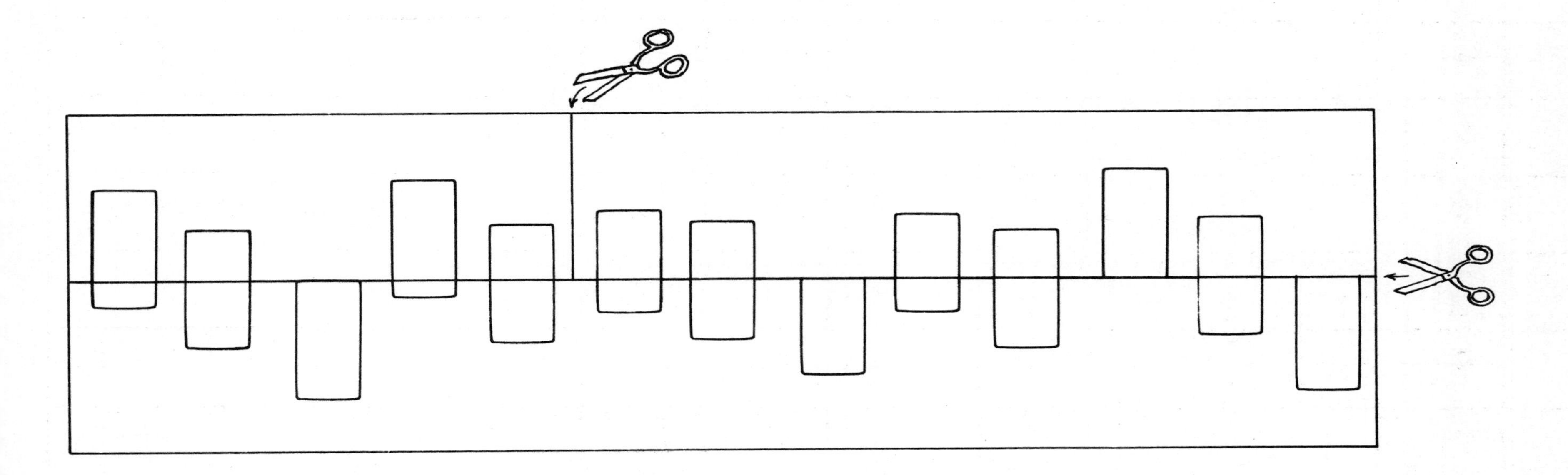

Interlocking magic squares, see page 91

24	11	3	20	7	24	11	3	20	7
5	17	9	21	13	5	17	9	21	13
6	23	15	2	19	6	23	15	2	19
12	4	16	8	25	12	4	16	8	25
18	10	22	14	1	18	10	22	14	1
24	11	3	20	7	24	11	3	20	7
5	17	9	21	13	5	17	9	21	13
6	23	15	2	19	6	23	15	2	19
12	4	16	8	25	12	4	16	8	25
18	10	22	14	1	18	10	22	14	1

Piece of card to cover 5 squares

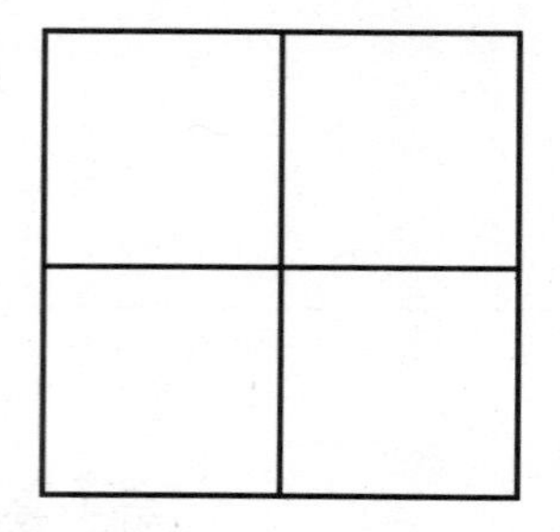

Piece of card to cover 4 squares

Optical illusions, see page 95

Turn the drawing upside down to find out what will happen if this person carries on eating too much.

Optical illusions, see page 95

Try to point to the top step – now try to point to the bottom step. This set of steps is impossible.

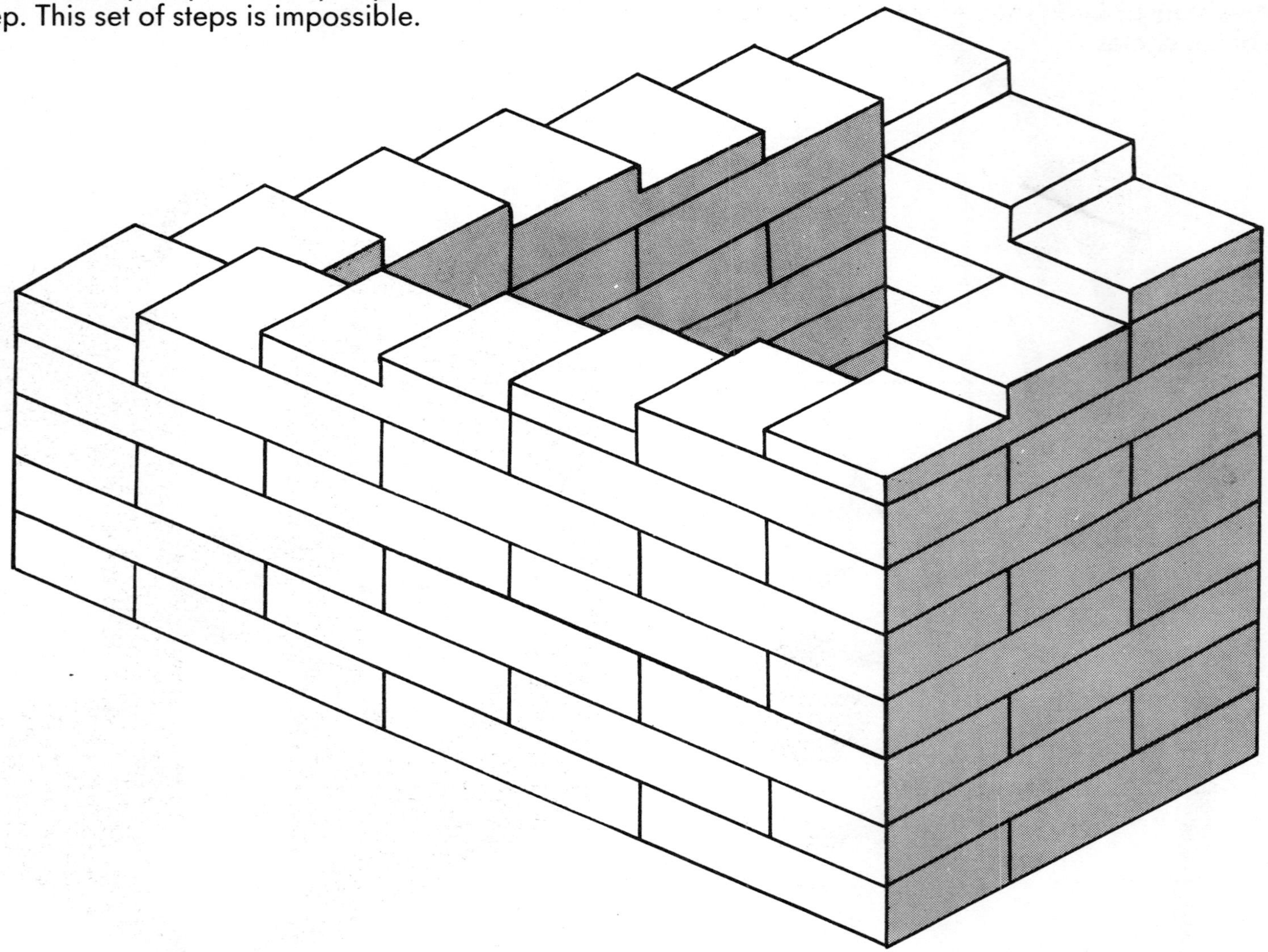

Optical illusions, see page 95

Can you see the white triangle? There isn't one there, but we see one that has been formed from the cut-outs of the small black circles.

Do you see this as four white arrows – or as a black letter 'H'?

Optical illusions, see page 95

This impossible elephant is very puzzling. Look at its legs – can your eyes figure them out?

What is your first impression – a mouse or someone's head?

Shadow pictures, see page 101

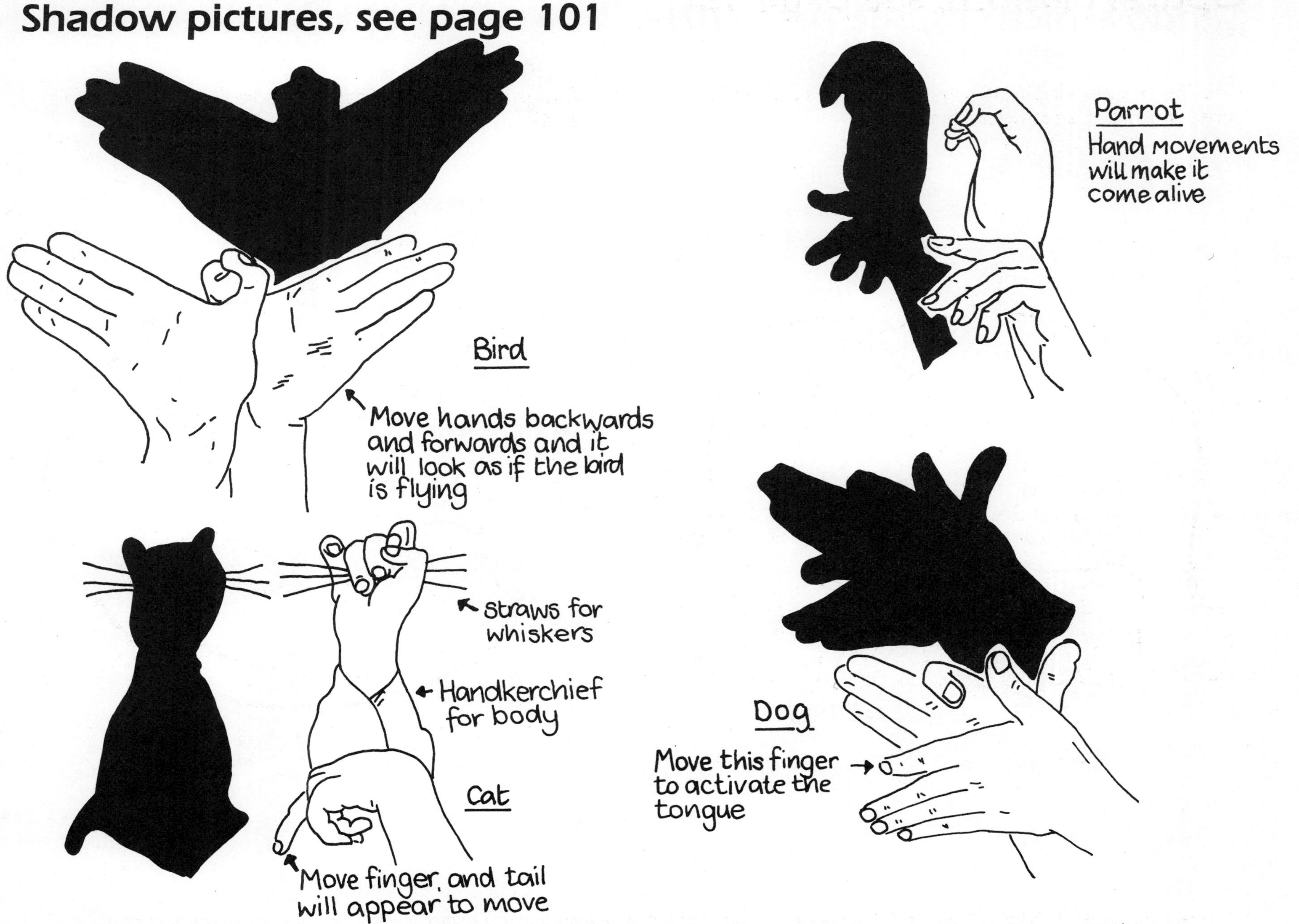

Shadow pictures, see page 101

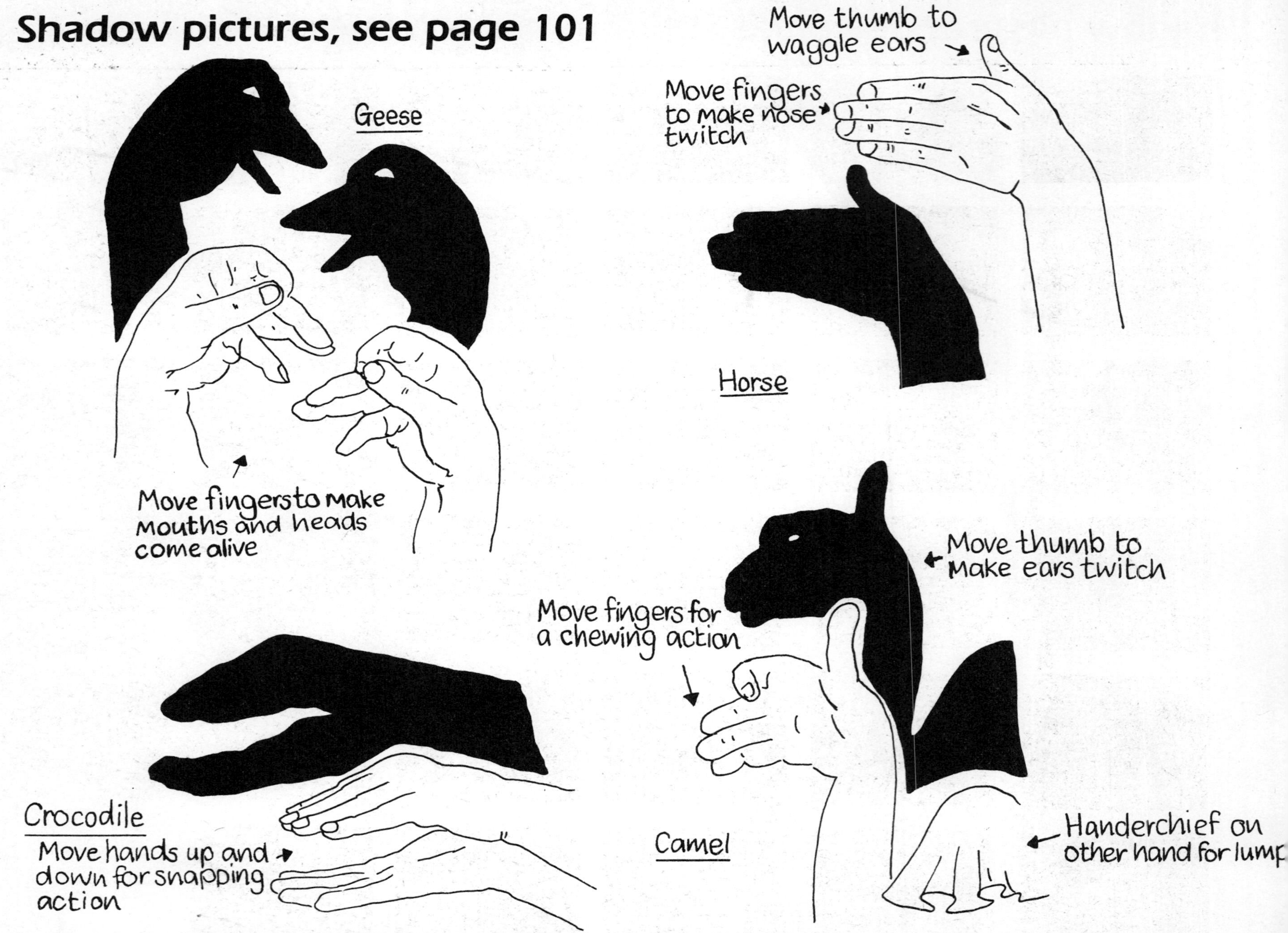